D0246779

MOVEMENT ILLUSIONS

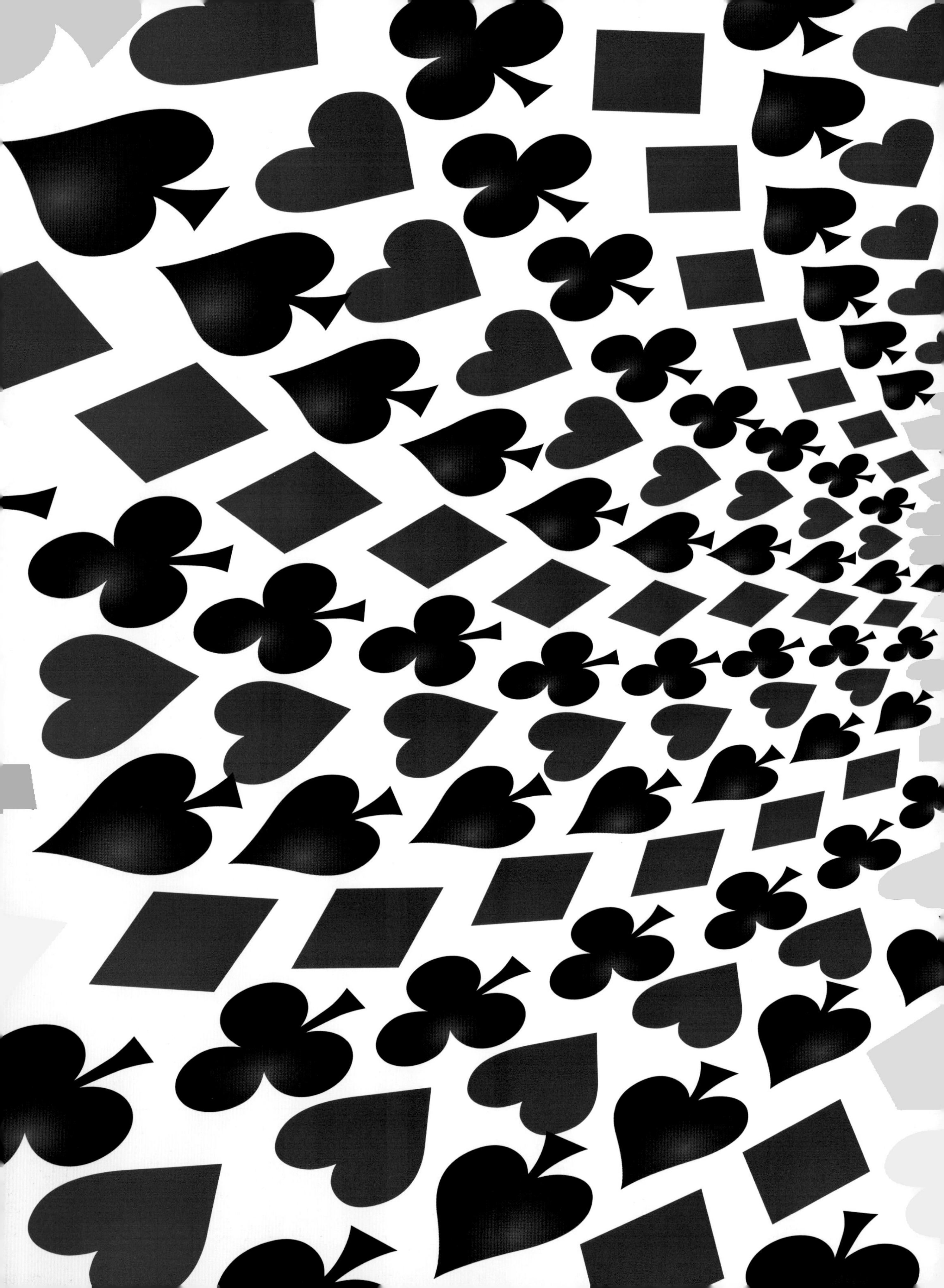

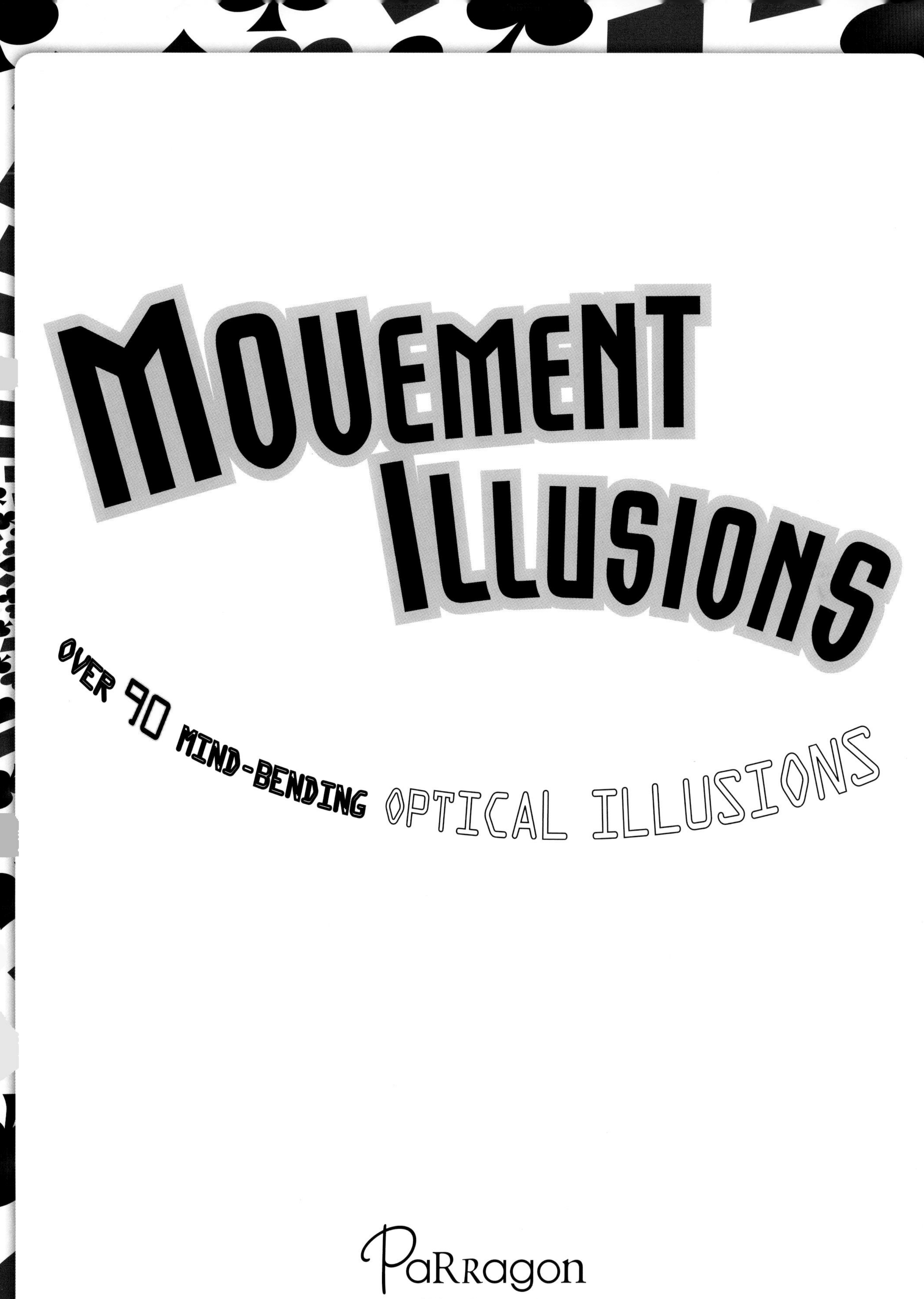

MOVEMENT ILLUSIONS

OVER 90 MIND-BENDING OPTICAL ILLUSIONS

Parragon

Bath • New York • Cologne • Melbourne • Delhi
Hong Kong • Shenzhen • Singapore • Amsterdam

First published by Parragon Books Ltd 2015

Parragon Books Ltd
Chartist House
15–17 Trim Street
Bath BA1 1HA, UK
www.parragon.com

Written and designed by Any Puzzle Media Ltd

ISBN 978-1-4748-0432-5

Printed in China

Get Ready to *Fly*

You might be still, but the pages in this book certainly aren't. Prepare to be moved.

From cover to cover, you'll encounter a huge range of movement illusions, of five main types:

3-D

These illusions make the page appear to contain separate layers, or even a full 3-D shape.

Chaotic

Images that move in many different directions are labelled in this way, and often contain a mix of other types.

Circular

Some illusions will appear to rotate on the page, or contain elements that appear to move in a circular pattern.

Expanding

This category includes both expanding and contracting illusions, which appear to get either larger or smaller.

Side-to-side

Some pictures contain elements that appear to slide in one direction, or sometimes in two opposing directions.

You don't need any special equipment to view each illusion – just yourself, and enough light that you can make out the contrasting colours on each page. Many of the illusions will start to move at the very moment you first see them, while some are a bit more reticent and may need coaxing to life. Read the viewing tip above each illusion to see if there is any specific guidance for that image.

If you have trouble seeing an illusion, here are a few techniques you can try:

- Try moving your eyes slowly up and down the image, or left and right across the image.
- Move your eyes in gentle clockwise or anticlockwise circles around the image.
- Some images work best when you move your eyes in a diagonal motion across the picture.
- Try moving the book further away from or closer to your eyes, and watch the illusion as you move it.
- Let your eyes go very slightly out of focus as you look at the illusion.

Space Invasion

As you look up and down the page, the aliens march back and forth in their rows.

Try looking at an alien invader in the top row, then move your eyes slowly down to one just below. You should see each row of invaders start to slide left or right, alternating in direction from top to bottom. Keep your eyes moving and so will the invaders! You may also find that as you read this text that you can see all of the alien ships swaying in the edge of your vision.

Around and Around

Let your eyes wander around the page and the image will rotate in both directions.

Eternal ***Expansion***

Is the picture below slowly expanding as you read this text?

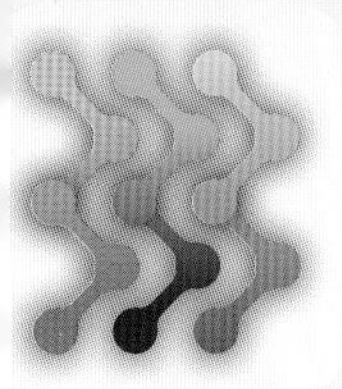

Shaking like ***Crazy***

Try running your gaze left to right and then up and down this mind-bending image!

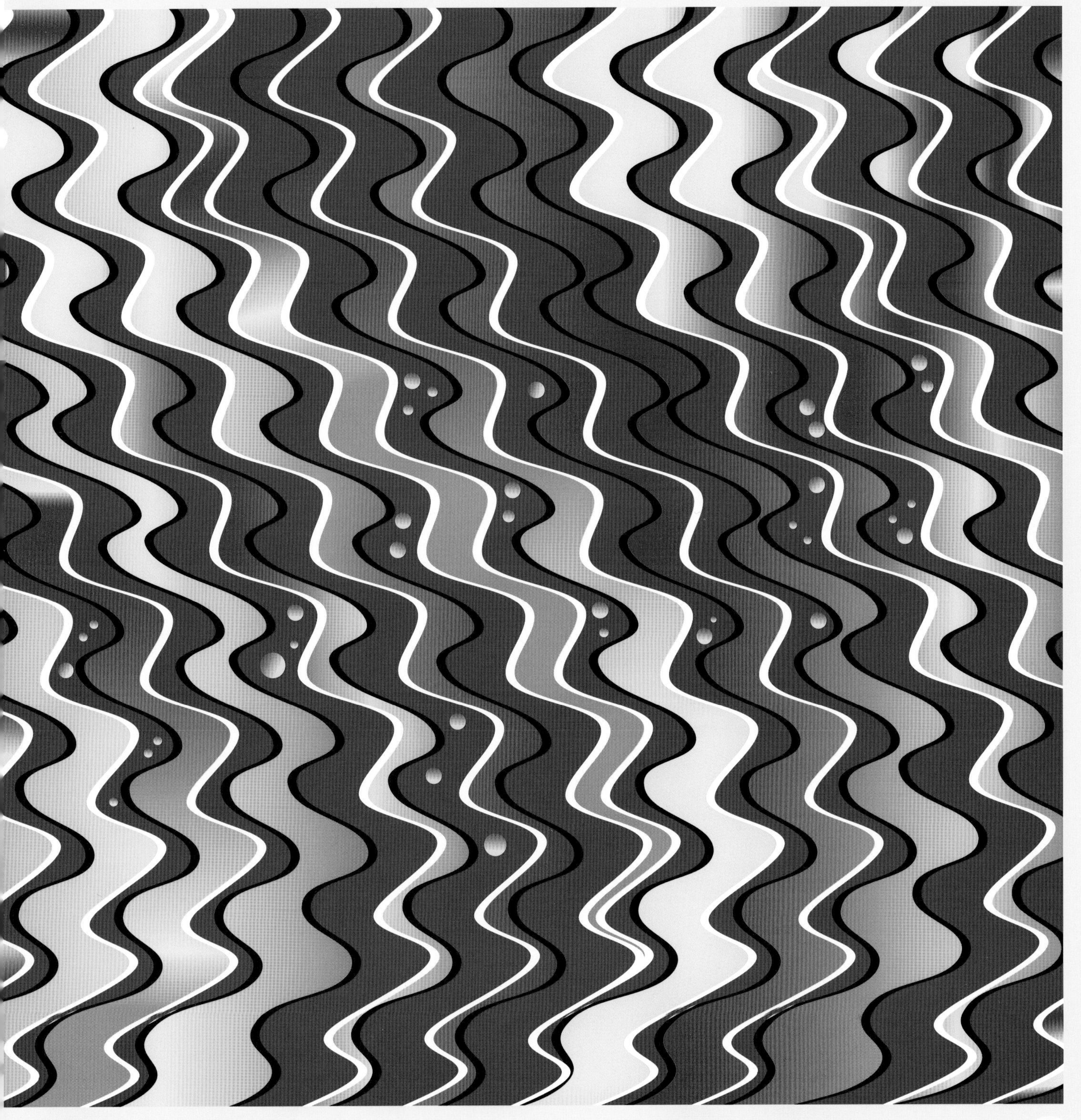

Jumping Out

Look to the side of the image and you should see the pattern spring out to get you!

Perpetual *Motion*

Do these floating spheres slowly rotate in space as you let your eyes wander?

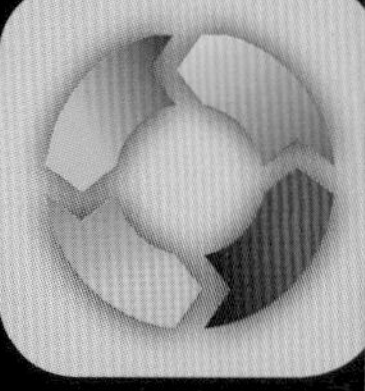

Summer *Spin*

As you look at each flower in turn, so you will see them start to spin.

Winter *Wobble*

Let your eyes drift around the page and the snowflakes will start to do the same.

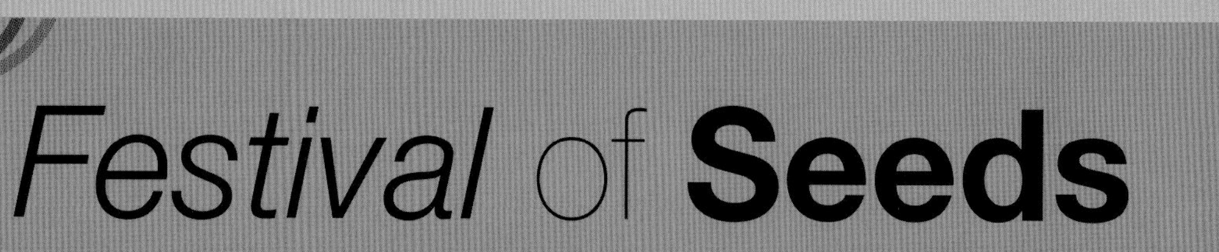

Festival of **Seeds**

Follow the fourth-outermost ring of seeds around the circle. What do you see?

As your eyes move around the perimeter of the image, you should see a flowing movement of all of the seeds as they seem to slowly creep about, shifting and moving in different ways.

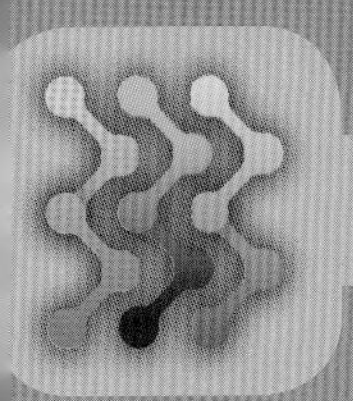

Beati**ng** Heart

Let your eyes wander around the red circles in the centre of this image.

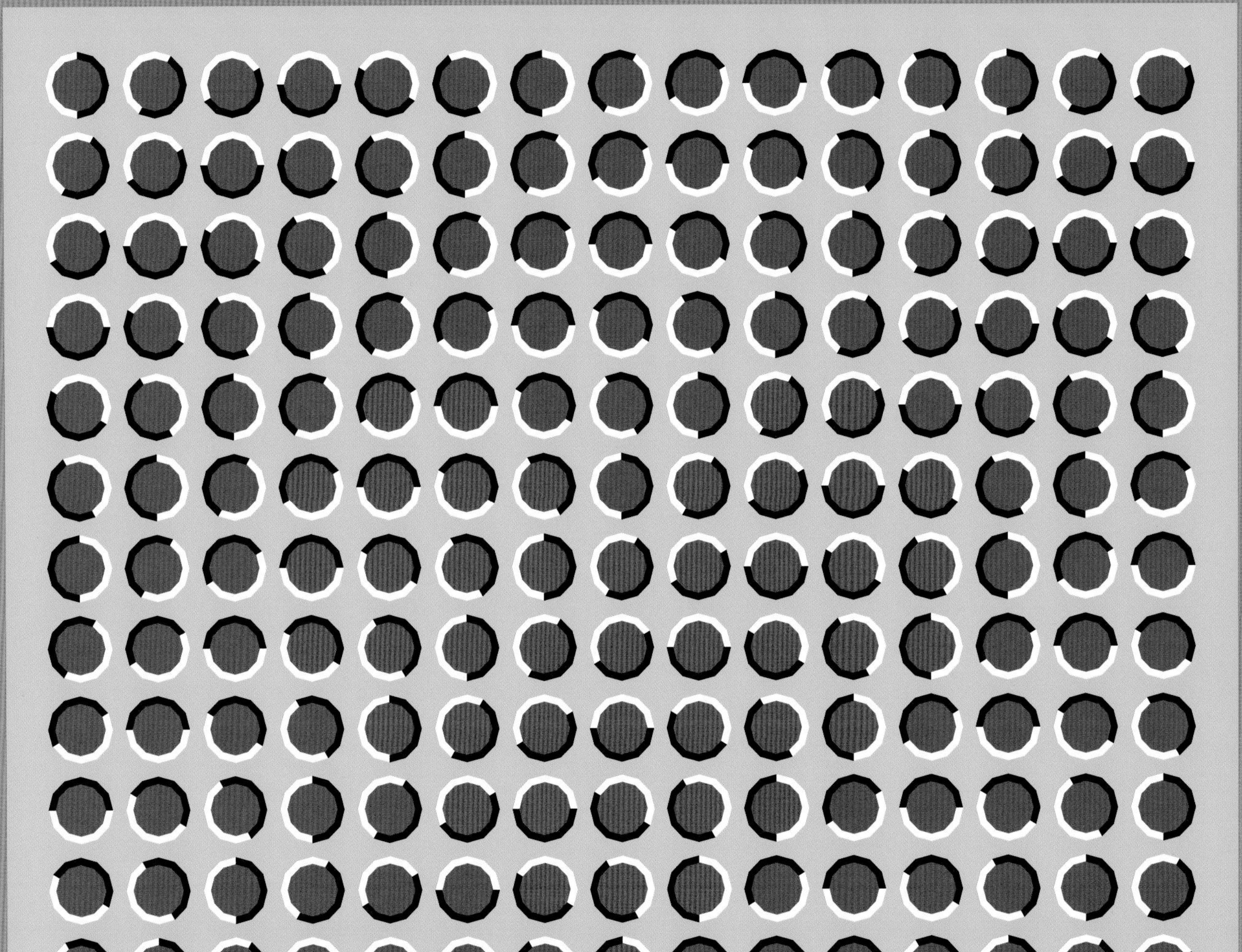

Even if you keep your eyes still, the sensation of movement in this image is so strong that the turbulent sea of blue circles will ripple and flow, no matter how much you try to convince yourself that this is merely an illusion! In fact, even as you read this text you'll see the image swaying to and fro!

Scintillating *Shimmer*

Move your eyes around each of these two images. What do you see?

In the image above, interference patterns appear with the interplay of the varying line widths in this pattern of black and white stripes. These create a vibrating, chaotic effect in which your eyes have trouble making sense of what they are seeing, and with no obvious point of interest they have trouble focusing on a particular spot.

The image on the opposite page also shimmers, but this time in a juddering, shaking way. The smooth colour gradations provide false movement cues, and the lack of any obvious place to focus once again makes it hard for your eyes to find a stable part of the image to settle on, resulting in a violent shuddering effect.

Em-anation

Move your eyes slowly down the page. As you do so, the discs of 'M's will rotate.

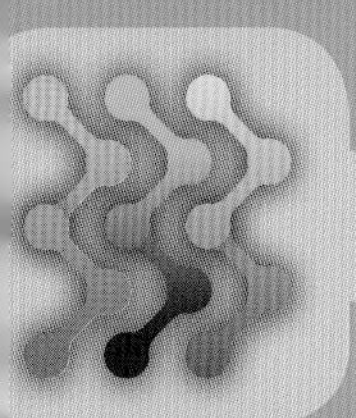

Sliding Along

Follow the arrows on these snakes with your eyes. Do the snakes seem to stir?

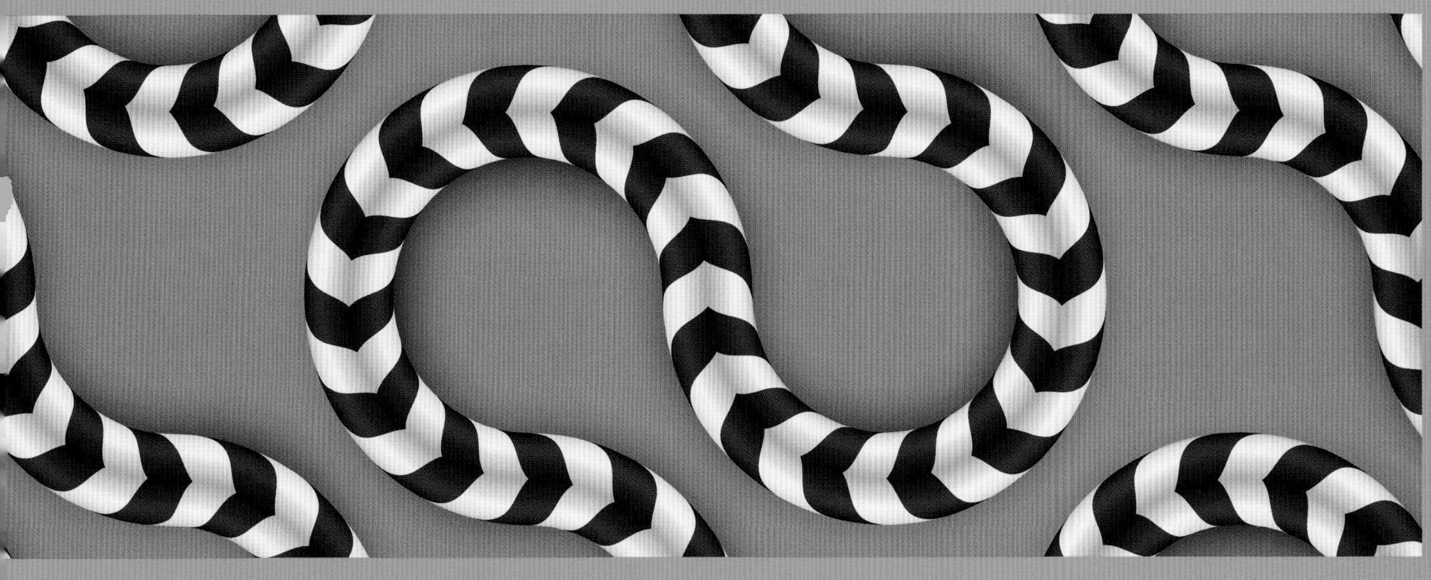

Stare into the centre of the image below and the pattern will start to swirl.

Stretching *and* Shrinking

As you move your eyes down the centre of the image, so it bulges and contracts!

An Issue of Alignment

Move your eyes up and down these columns of squares. Do they slide about?

These two illusions work because your brain is trying to line up the misaligned squares, creating a sense of movement.

Swaying Mushrooms

Run your eyes up and down this image. Do the mushrooms sway?

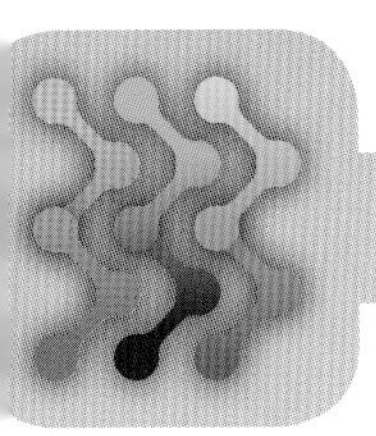

Pulsing Patterns

Let your eyes wander freely around each of these two images.

Despite the simplicity of the grid pattern to the left, the shapes seem to bulge and roll along in diagonal groups as you move your eyes around the picture.

In the image to the right, the circular shape to the top left seems to float in front of the background, which is jumping past that shape in jerky, sudden movements.

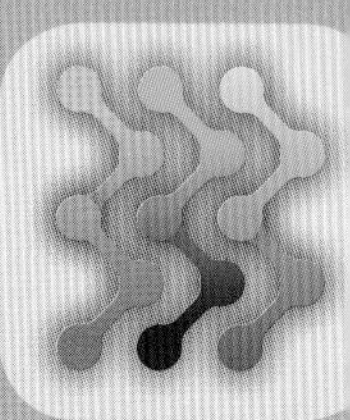

Lapping Lapwings

As you look at each bird, so the others fly around in a twisting, sliding formation.

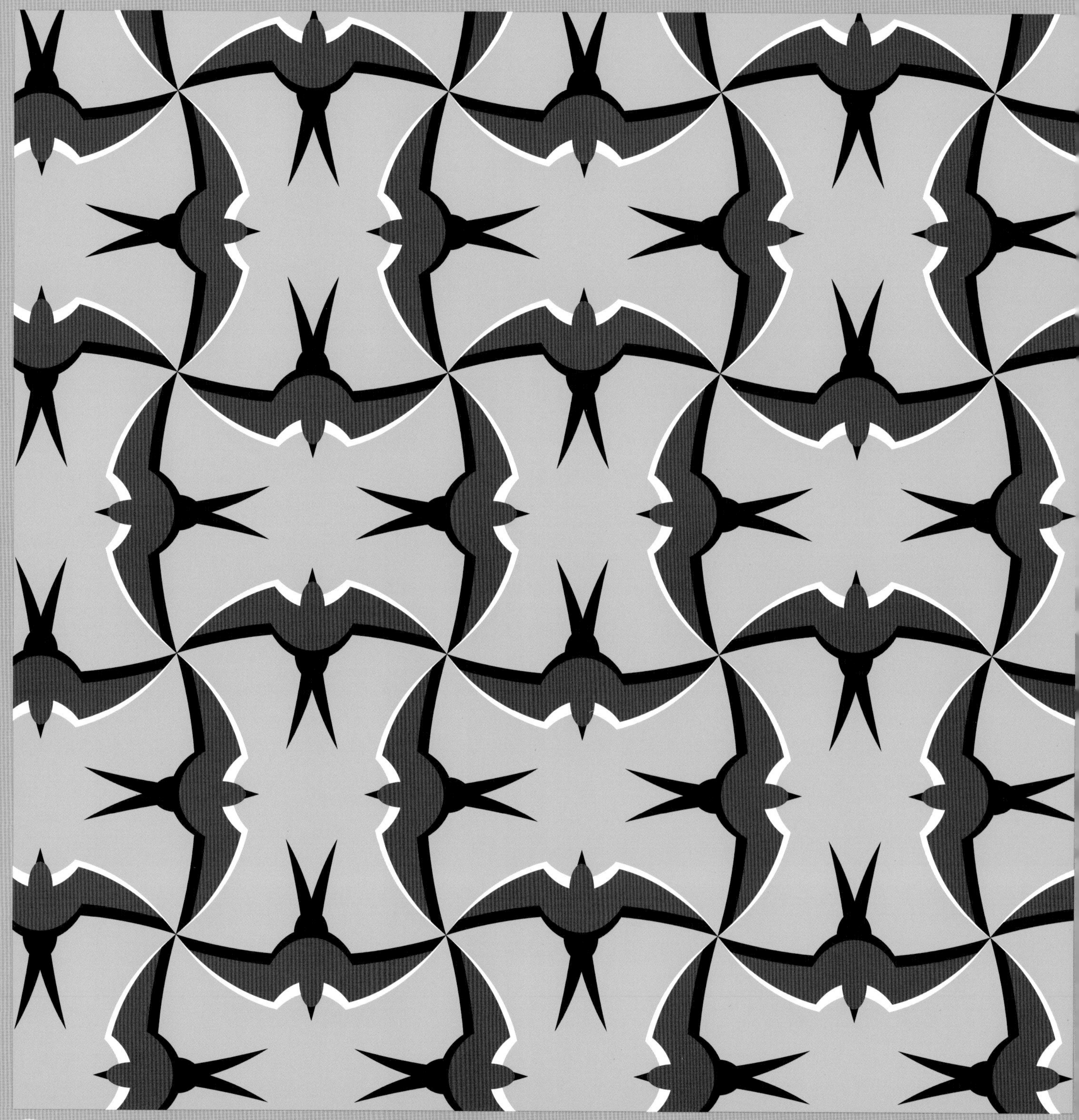

Floral *Flourish*

Let your eyes wander in slow circles around the page, watching the flowers unfurl.

City *Escape*

As you read this text, you'll see the rings of buildings start to slowly revolve.

Struggling to **Fit**

As you look around this page, the rows of chevrons sway in and out of the book.

Folk *Dance*

Look up and down the page and the lines of dancers will sway into rhythmic life.

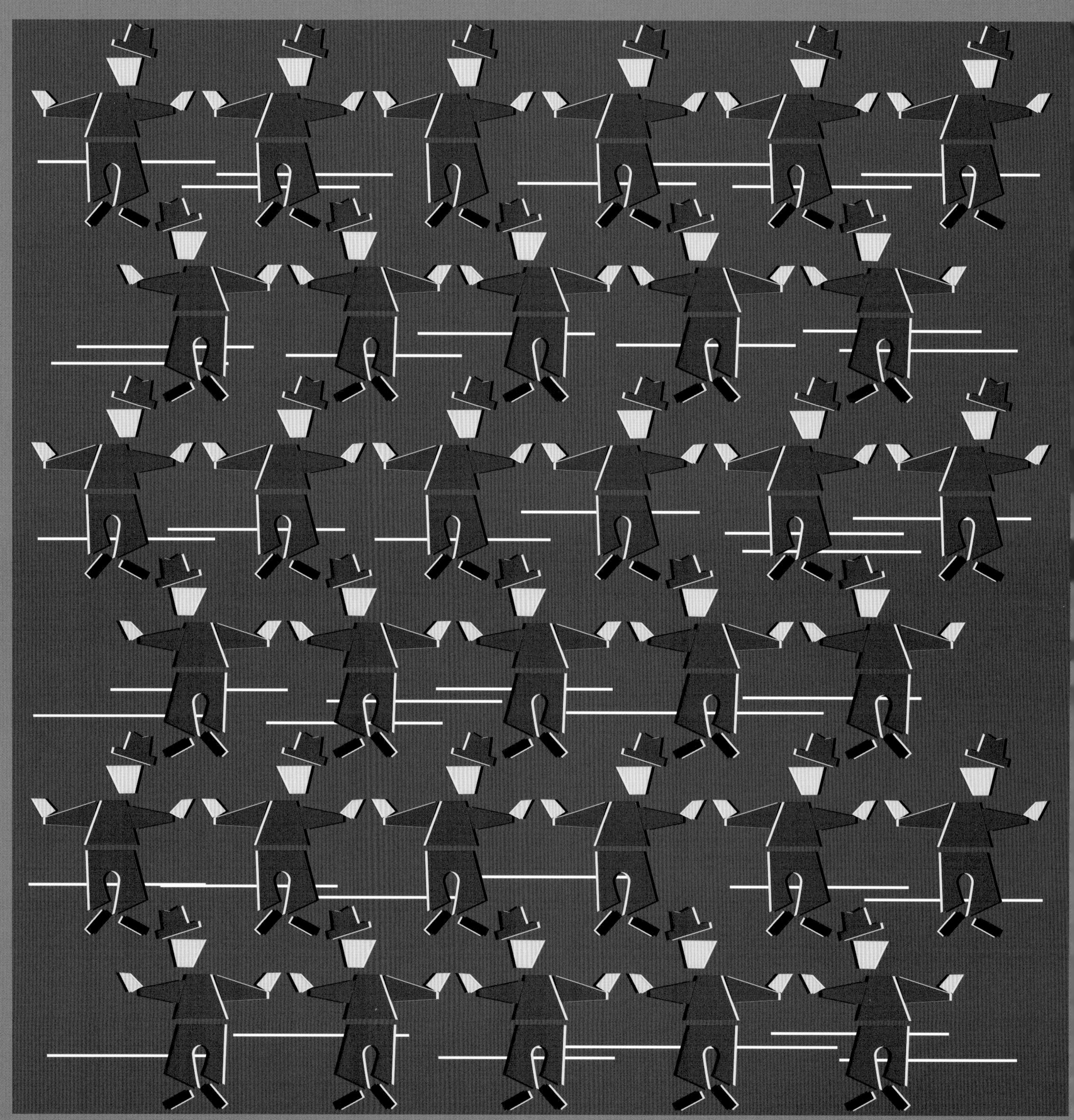

A-mazing ***Movement***

Move your eyes left to right across the top of this image, and the mazes separate.

Blowing Bubbles

Look at one bubble, then another, and another, as they float around the page.

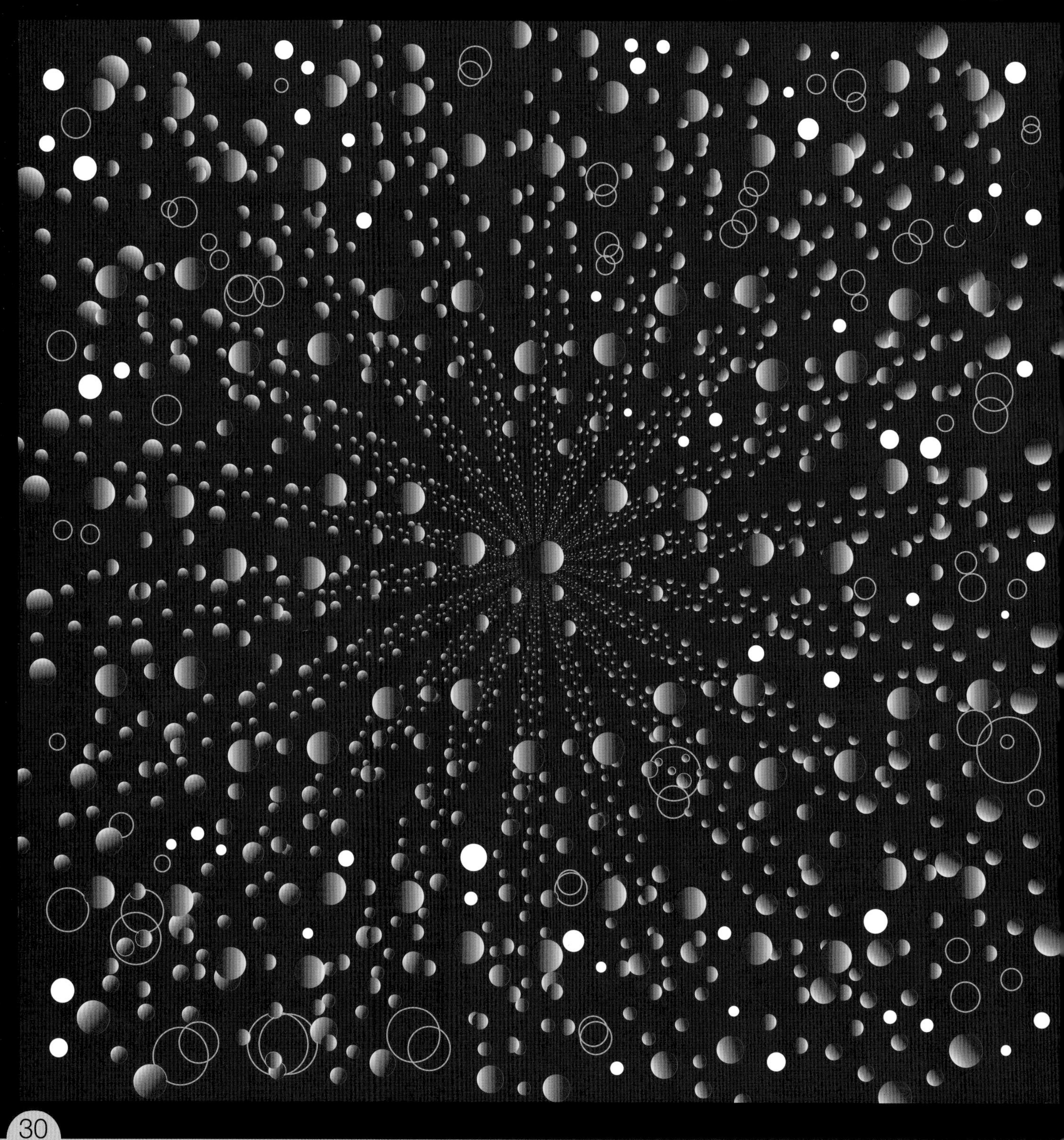

Pulsing **Peacock**

The exotic plumage on this bird will hypnotize you if you dare to look at it!

They're **Alive!**

Look from centre to centre of these cells and they will seem to breathe in and out.

Portal to **Another Dimension**

Look at the right-hand edge of the page, and the portal will start to activate.

Boxing **Clever**

As you look at each group of boxes, so the others will start to spin.

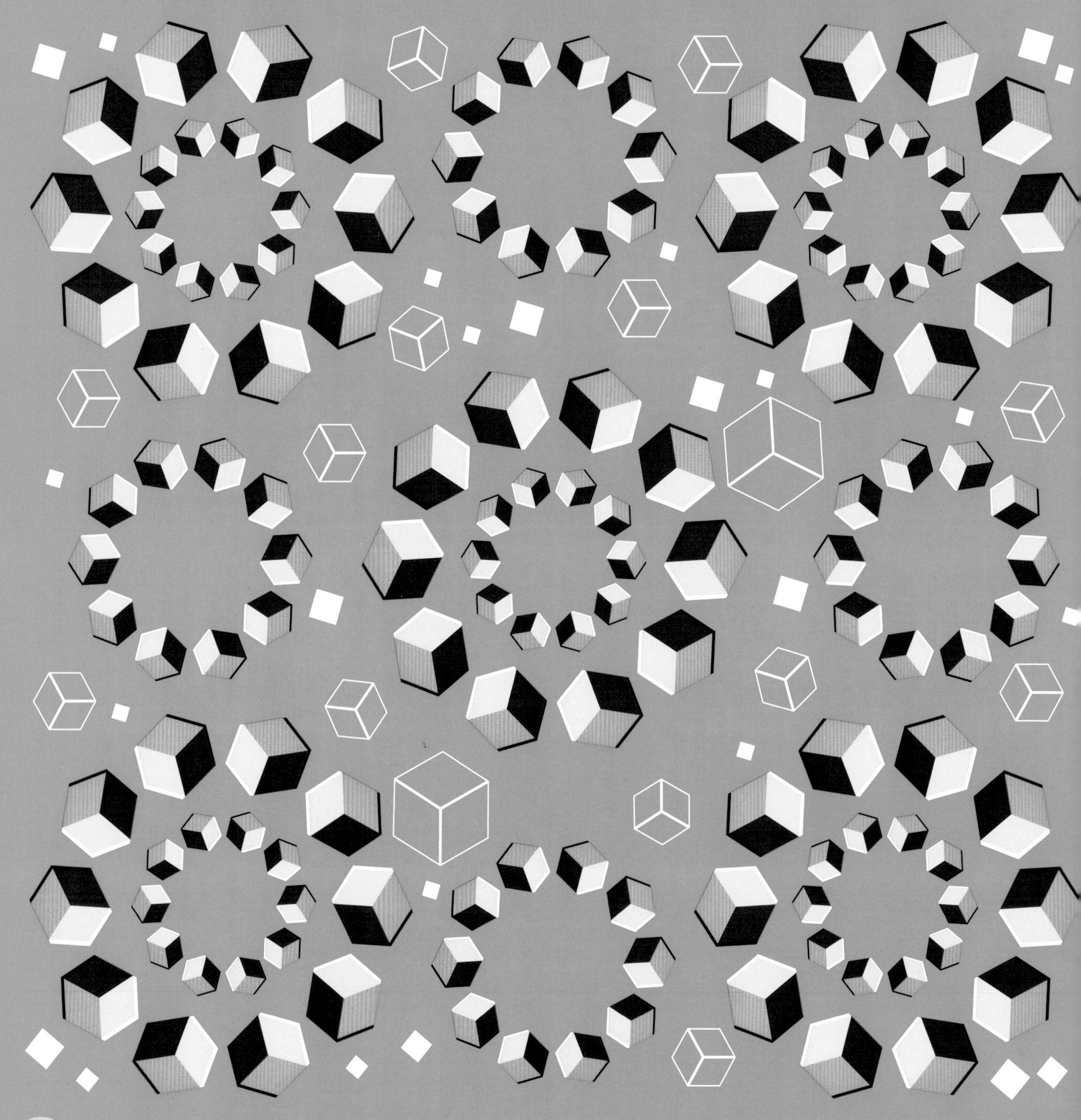

Flying Free

Look at the body of the butterfly and you will feel it floating through the air.

As you look at the centre of this butterfly, or read this text, you will have the strong sensation of the butterfly gently floating down. The overall effect of it travelling through space can be uncannily convincing.

Some **Expansion** Required

Look at the centre of the image. The outer squares expand, compacting the centre

Around and ***About***

Slowly move your eyes in clockwise circles around the image, and it will rotate.

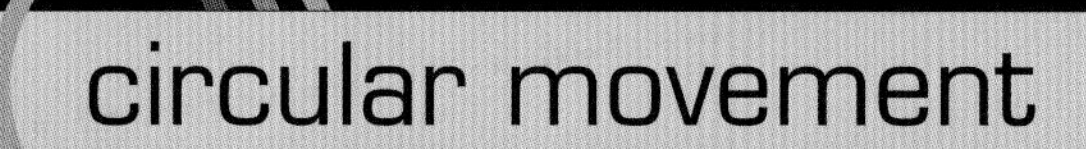

Enter the *Mixer*

As you look to the edge, then to the centre, the mixer starts to turn. Don't fall in!

Do Not Adjust Your Set

This pattern seems to buzz with energy, no matter where you look.

It's **Watching You**

Move your head towards and then away from the page. The tunnel is alive!

Pattern *Phenomena*

Move your eyes left to right and then right to left across these patterns.

The columns in the image below appear to slide up and down as your eyes move left and right.

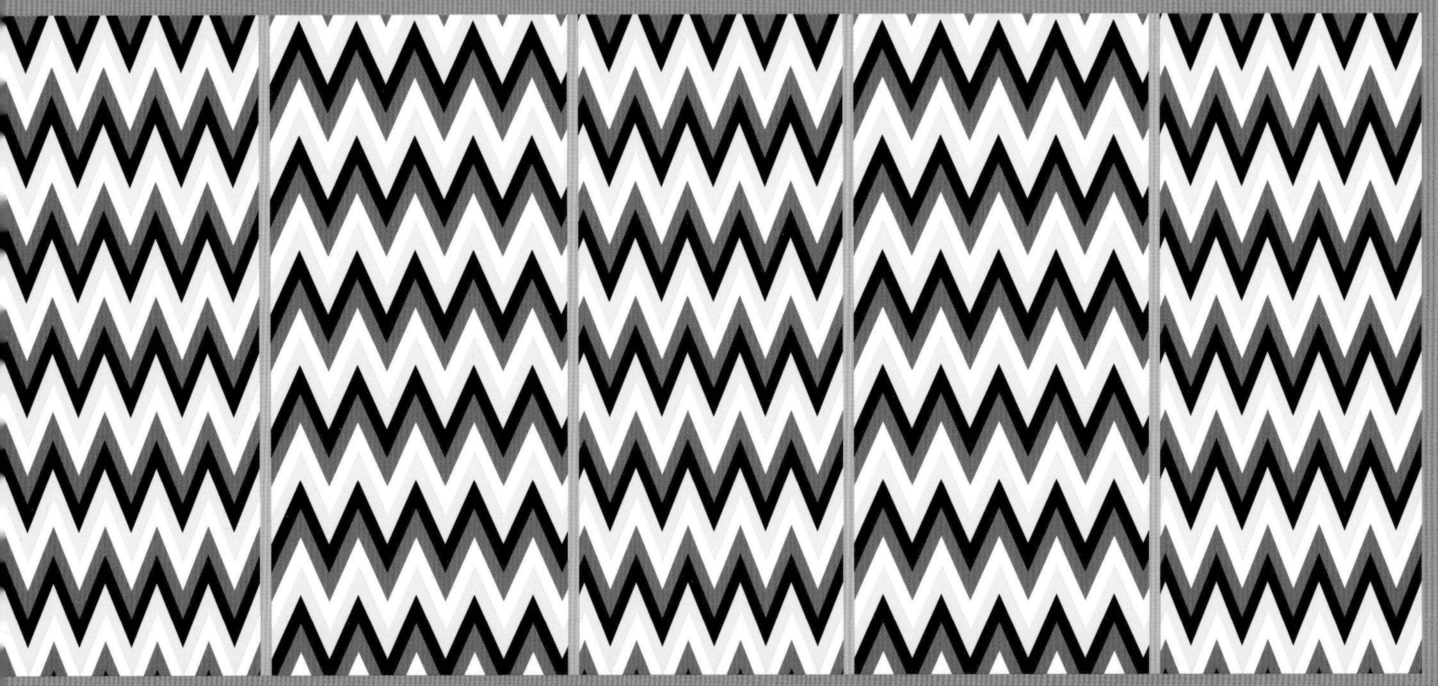

These columns of chequers undulate as your eyes move across, in a most surprising fashion!

Don't Get *Stung*

Let your eyes drift around the page, as the jellyfish drift with the current.

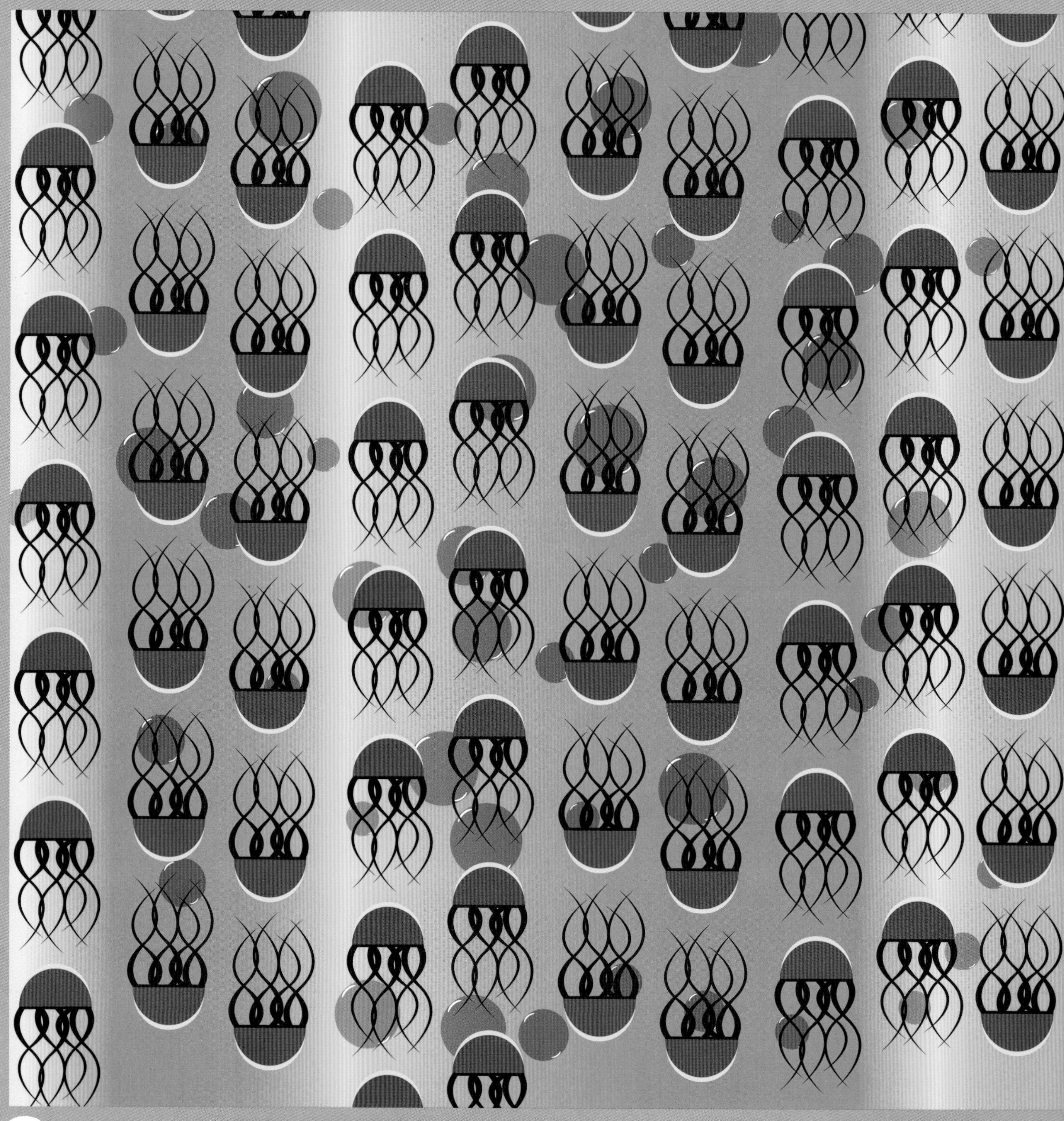

Flower **Power**

It may look like a perfect flower, but move slowly closer and it will start to expand.

Spiralling In

Try tracing the spiral into the centre, and you'll soon start spinning with the page.

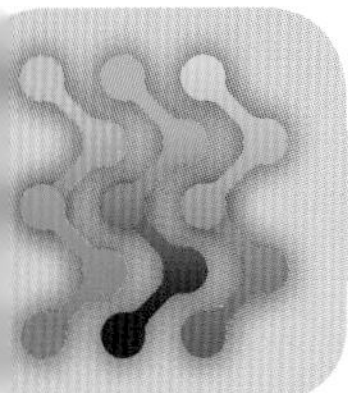

Shake Some **Flakes**

Run your eyes around the edge of this image, and watch the red flakes shake.

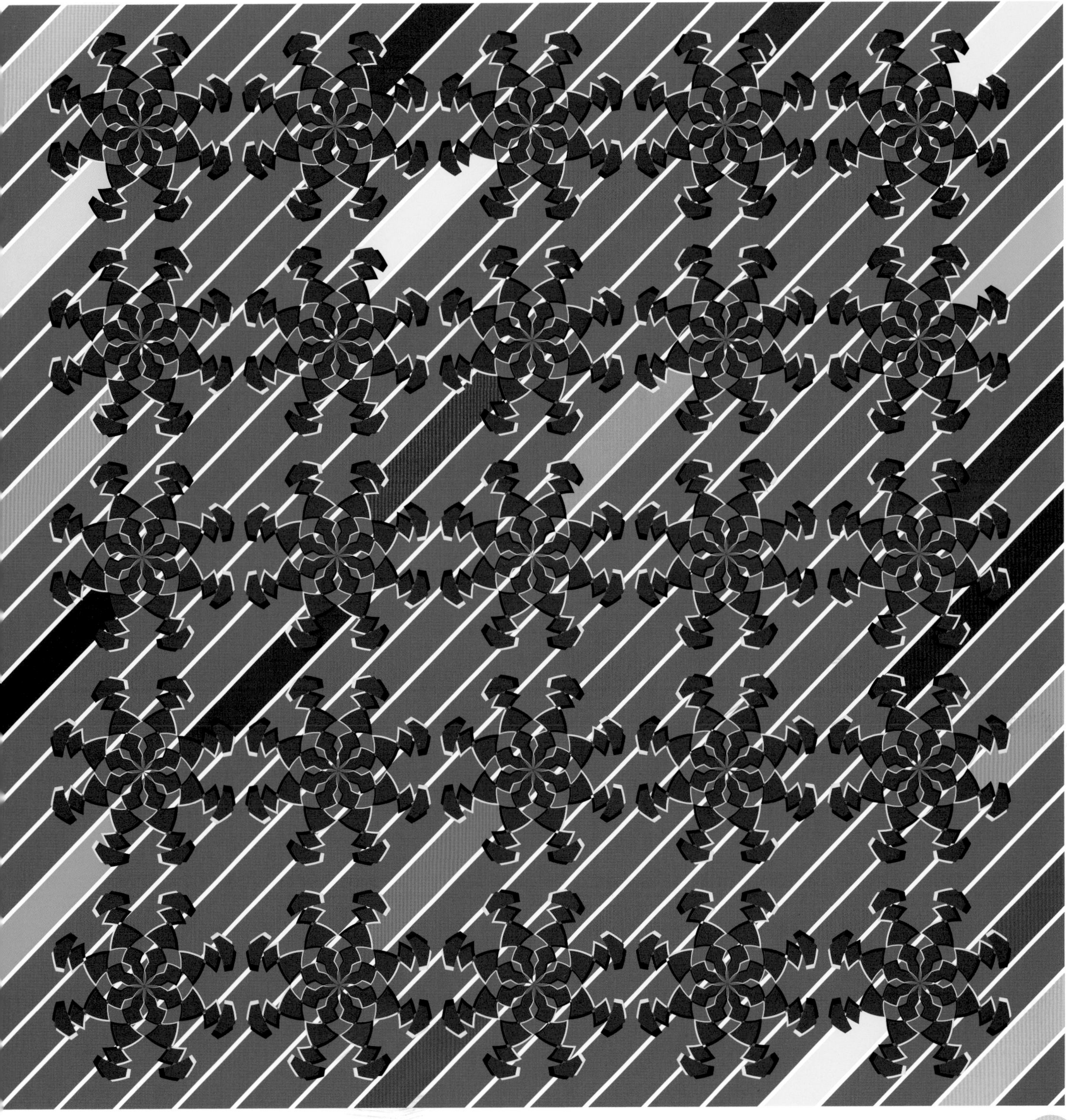

Meadow **Movement**

Look from the butterflies to the flowers, and then back. The meadow's alive!

In Orbit

Look at the centre of this image, and observe the outer circles orbit in their rings.

The Vortex

Whatever part of this image you look at, it inexorably draws you in.

Blooming *Blossom*

Look at the centre of this image, then away to this text. The plant will start to grow!

Under Undulation

As you look at this image, it appears to rise and fall, as if drifting on a breeze.

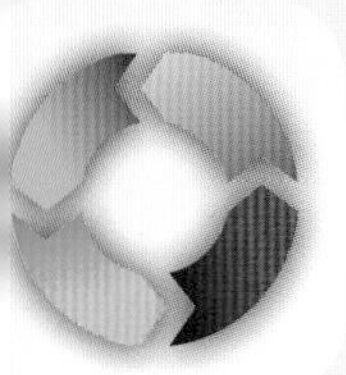

A Flock in *Flight*

Look up and down the image – can you see the birds rotating in formation?

Rush Hour

Get this traffic moving by looking quickly from car to car.

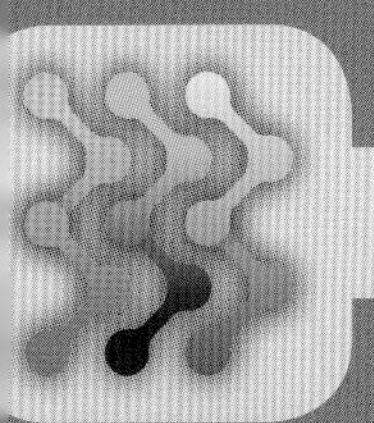

It's a Bug's Life

These creatures only scuttle across the page when you're not looking...

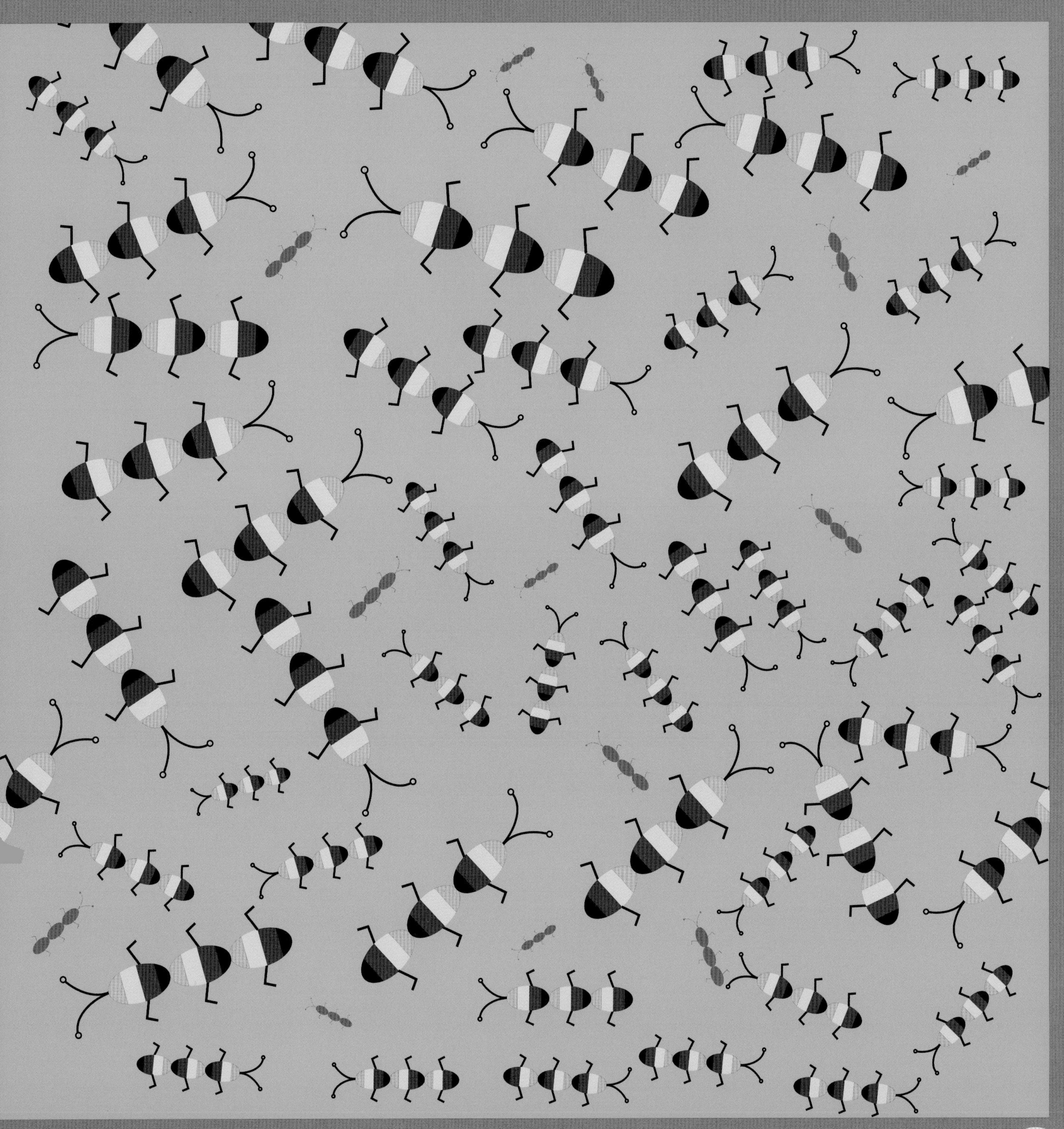

Seasonal *Swaying*

Look up and down the rows of decorated trees, and they'll gently sway.

Spinning Snow

Look at the slowly drifting snow. Each flake spins as it floats through the air.

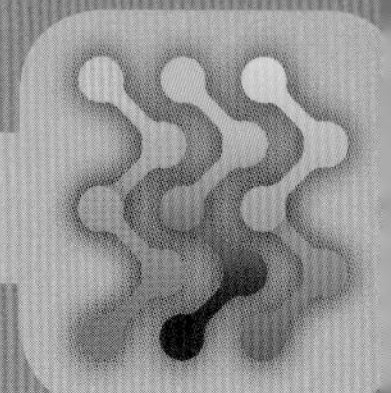

Wobbling Waves

Look at these dots until your eyes go out of focus. Do they start to pulse?

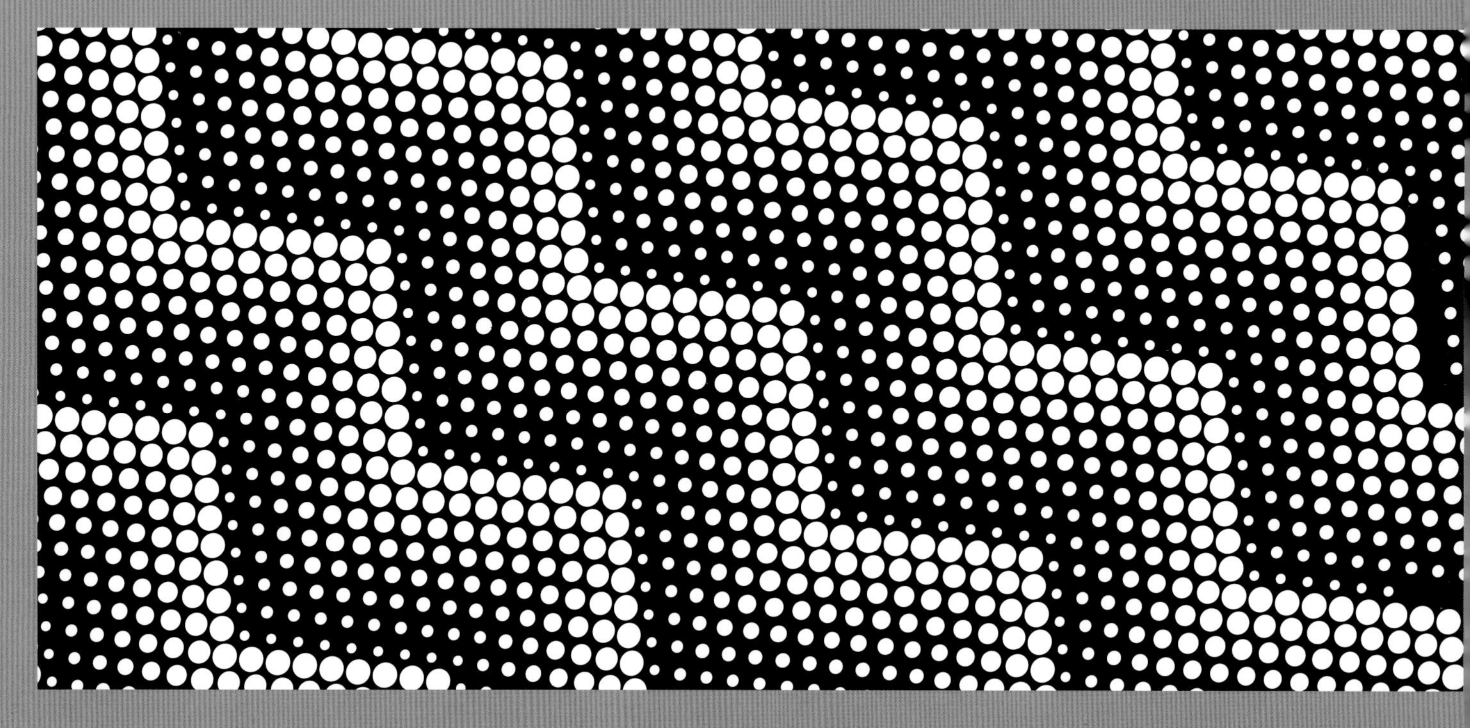

Trace a path between squares with your eyes, and watch them drift around.

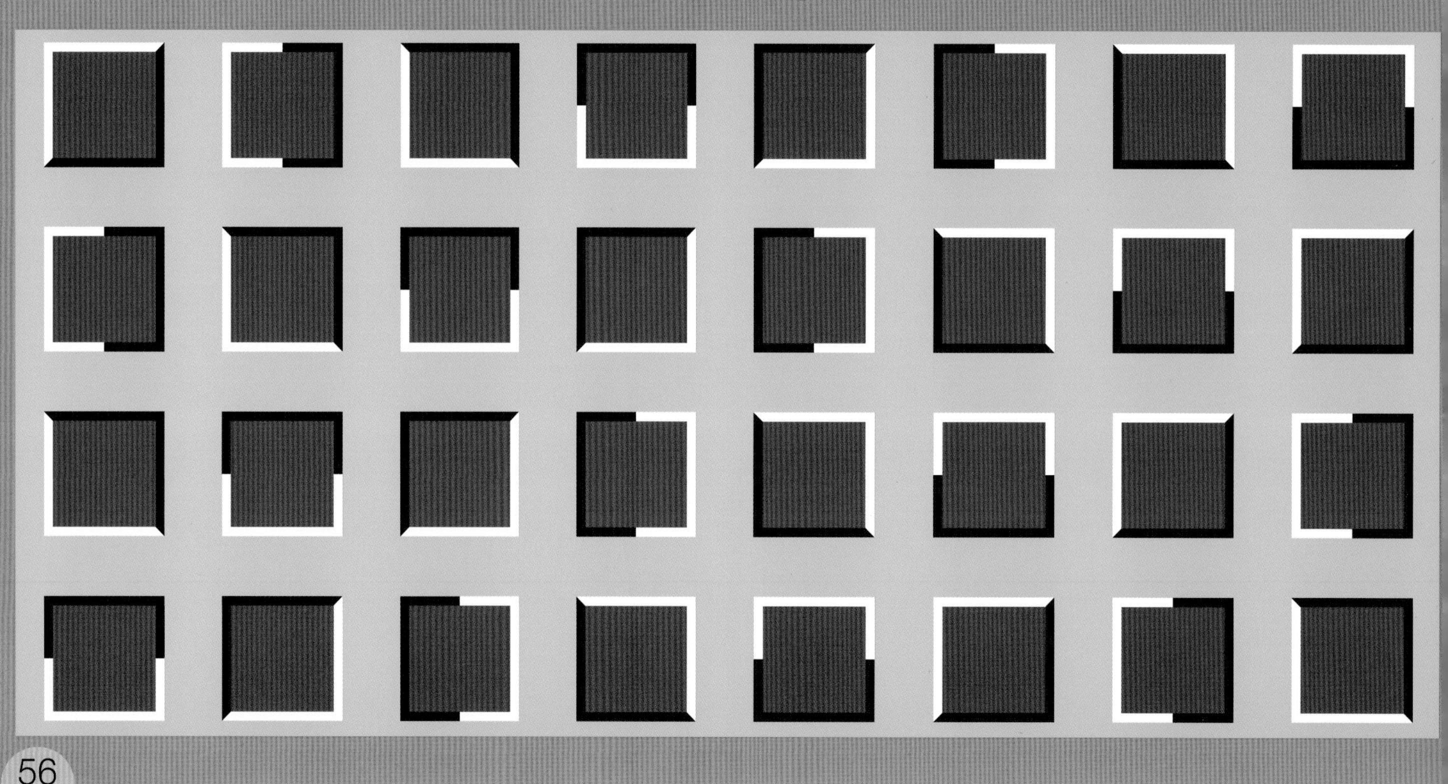

Ball *Bolero*

As you look at the surface of these balls, their surfaces seem to morph and turn.

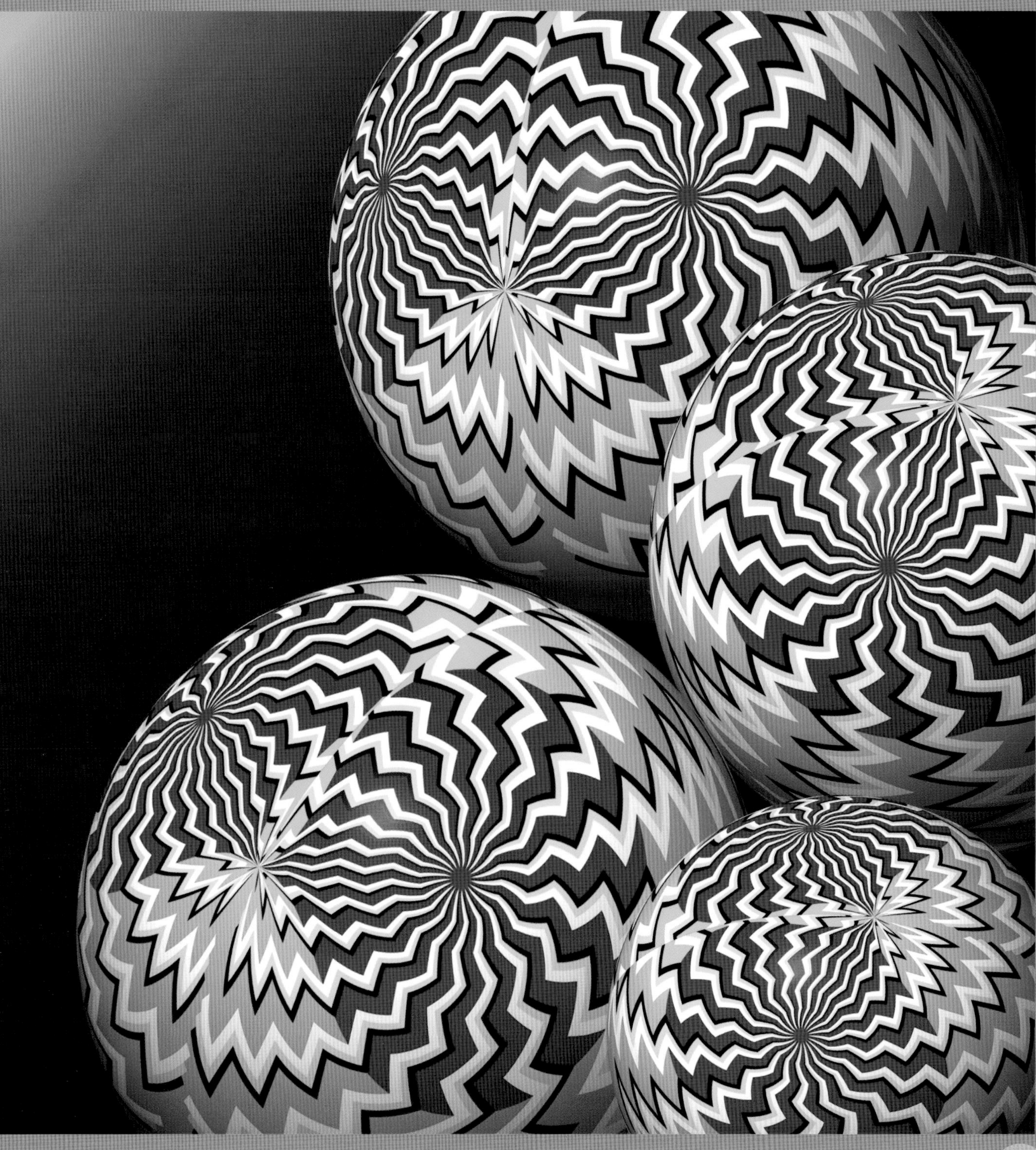

A Movable Feast

Just looking at these candles makes them move – they don't even need wind!

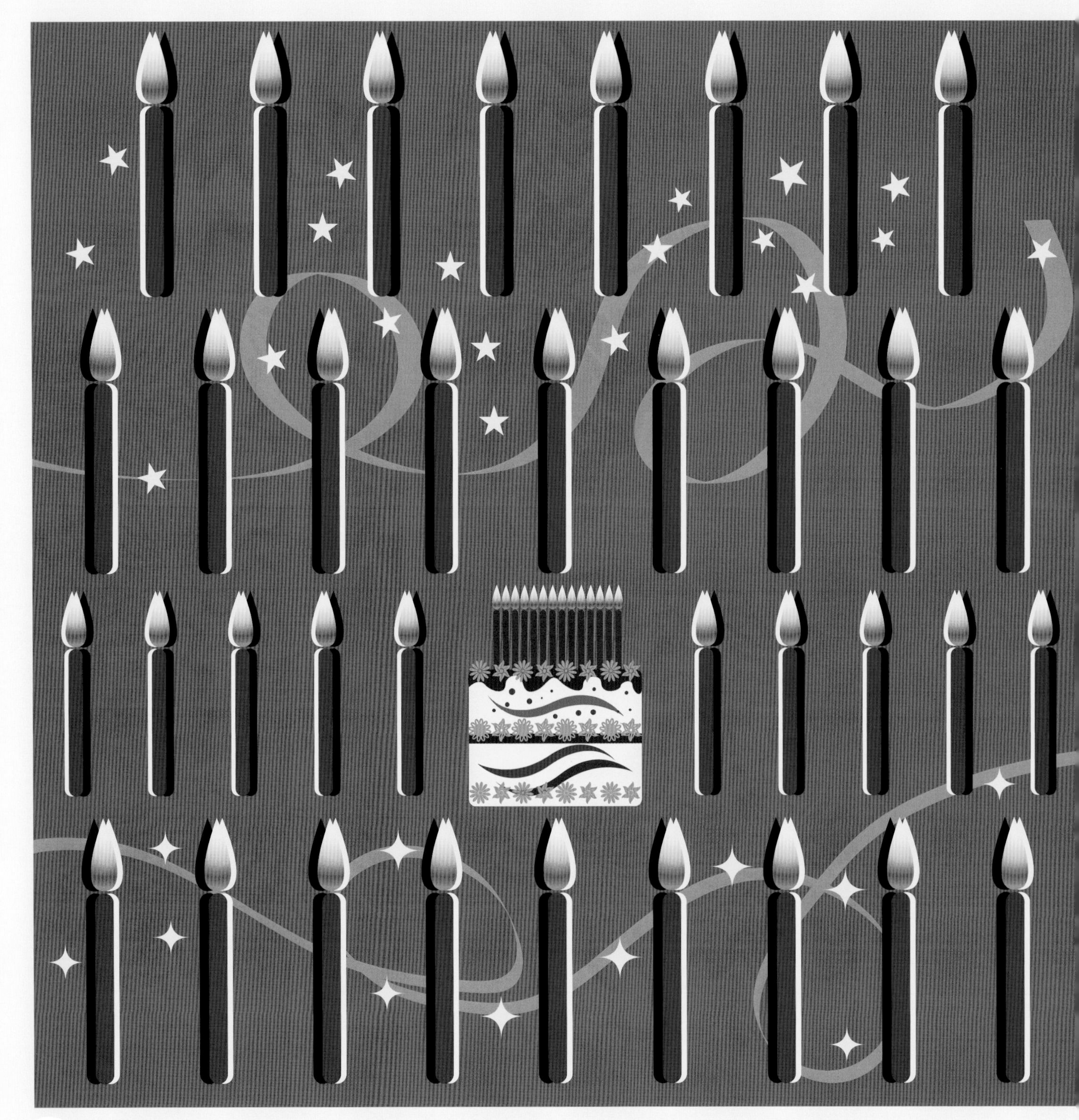

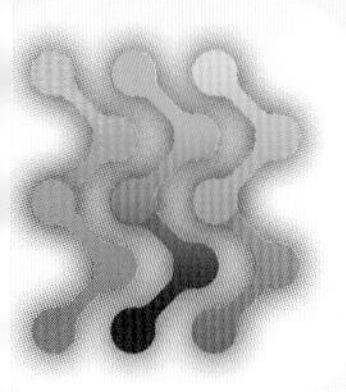

Creature Feature

Can you make the snakes crawl and the fish swim?

f you look steadily at a part of a snake, then look steadily at another part and so on, you should see the snakes start to move.

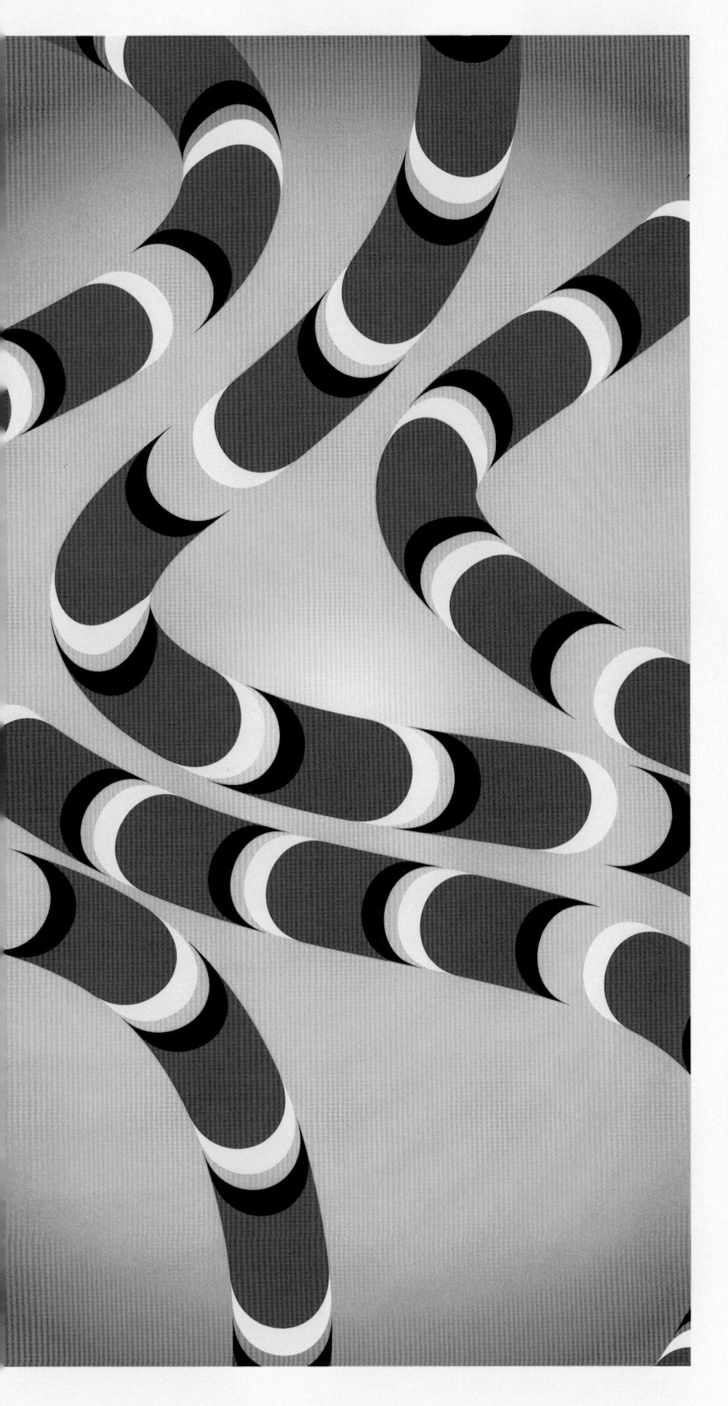

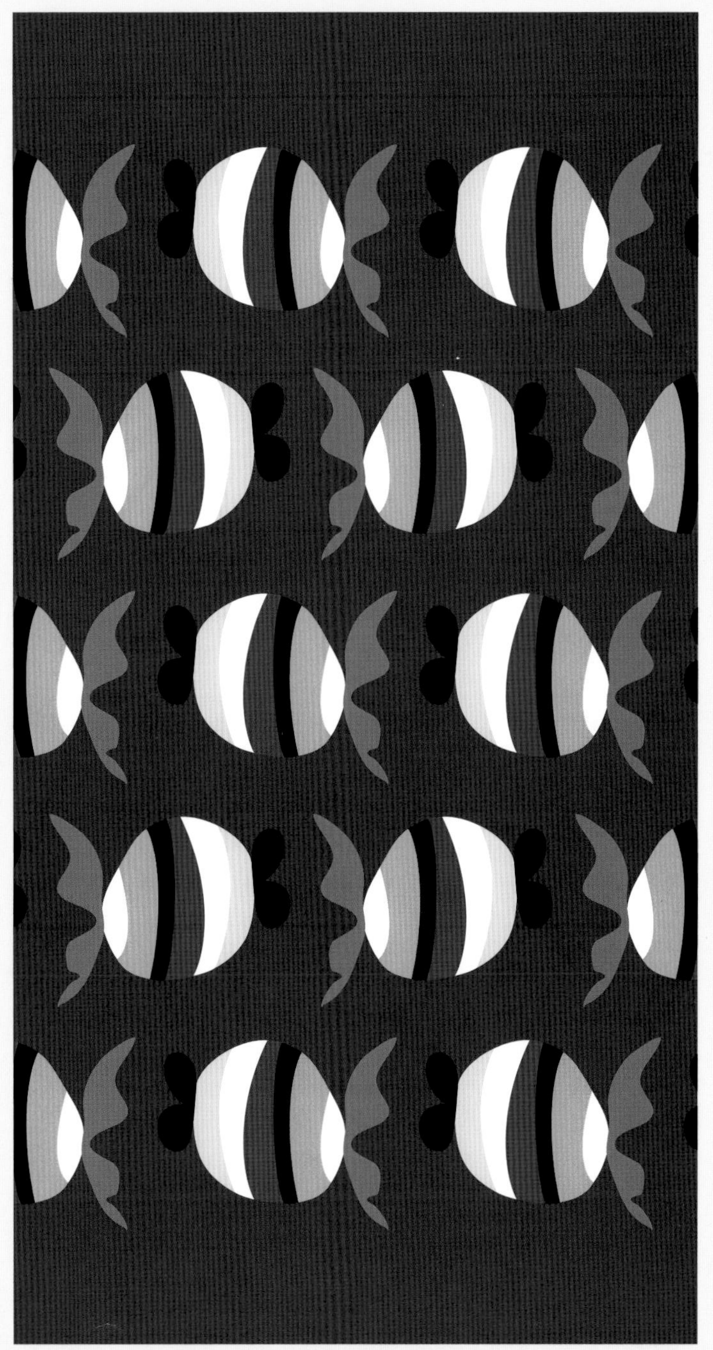

As you read this text, glance up at the fish and then back to the text. Can you see them swimming out of the corner of your eye?

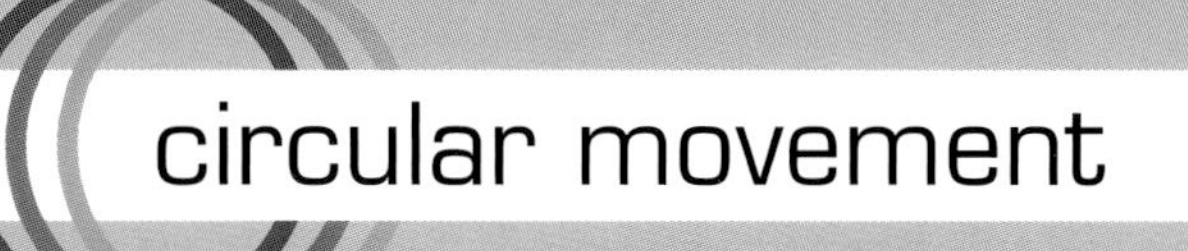

Spin Power

These lines both rotate and shimmer. Now try moving the page rapidly closer too!

Wheel of **Attraction**

However you look at this image, it will mesmerize you and slowly suck you in...

Revenge of the **Invaders**

Scan the purple sky. The invaders are floating down. There's no stopping them.

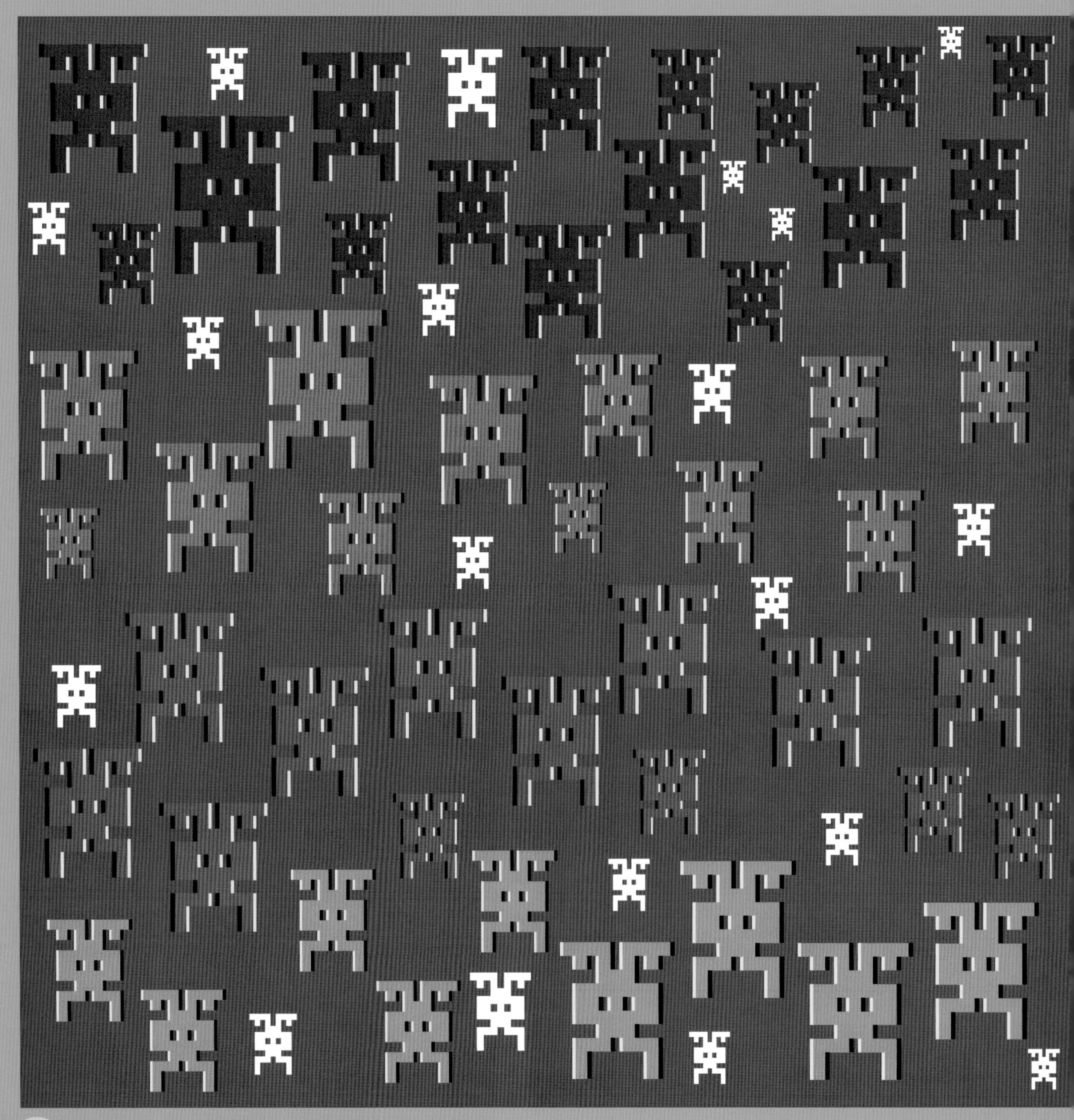

Festival *Fever*

As you view these colourful plumes, they sway as if in a Mardi Gras parade.

Shimmering *Motion*

Look at the centre of a swirling shape, then another. Do they shimmer and shake?

Floating **Free**

As you view this image, do you see the background floating past in the distance?

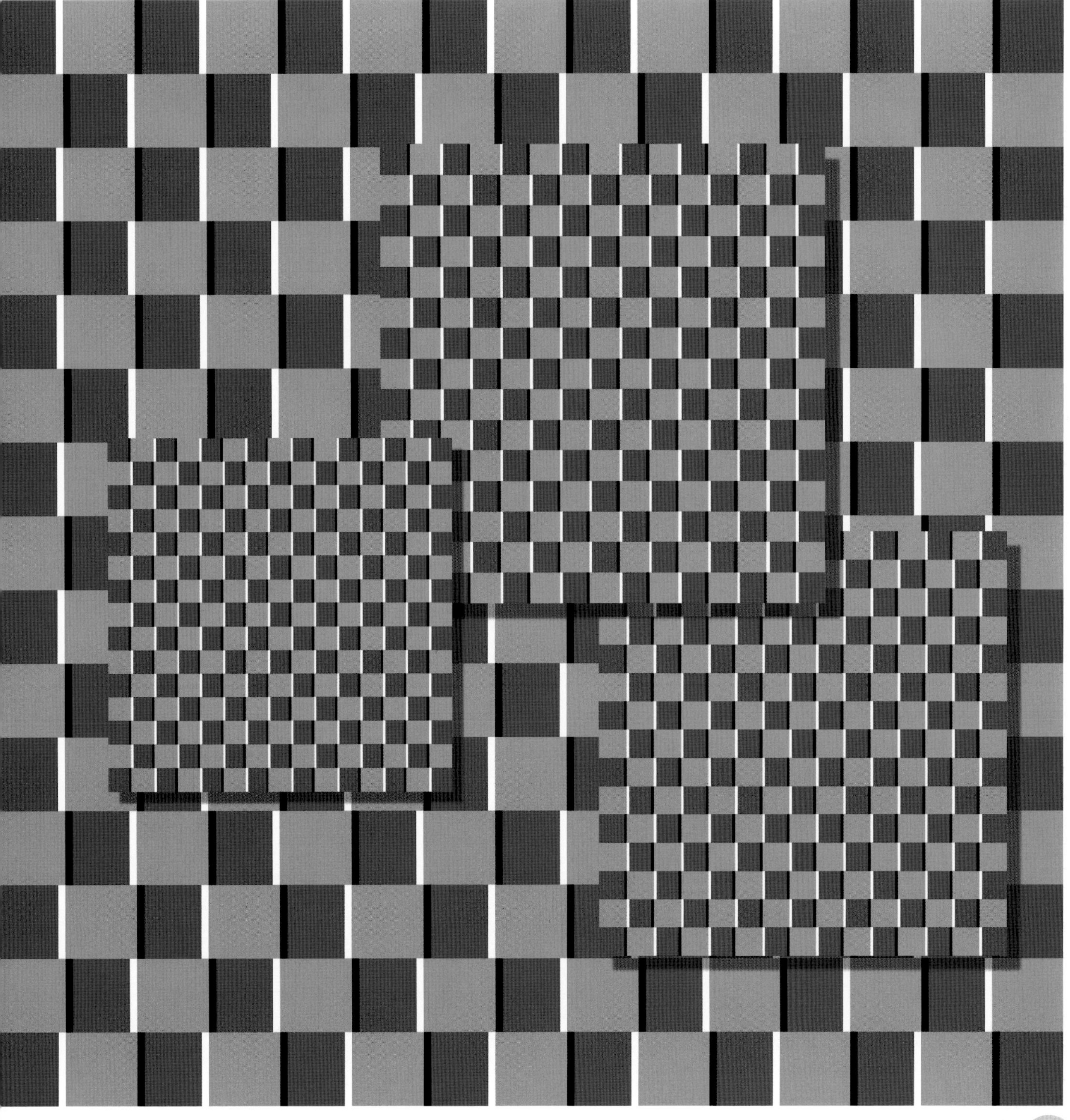

'V' is for *Revolution*

Follow the outer ring of 'V's in the direction they point. They're on the march!

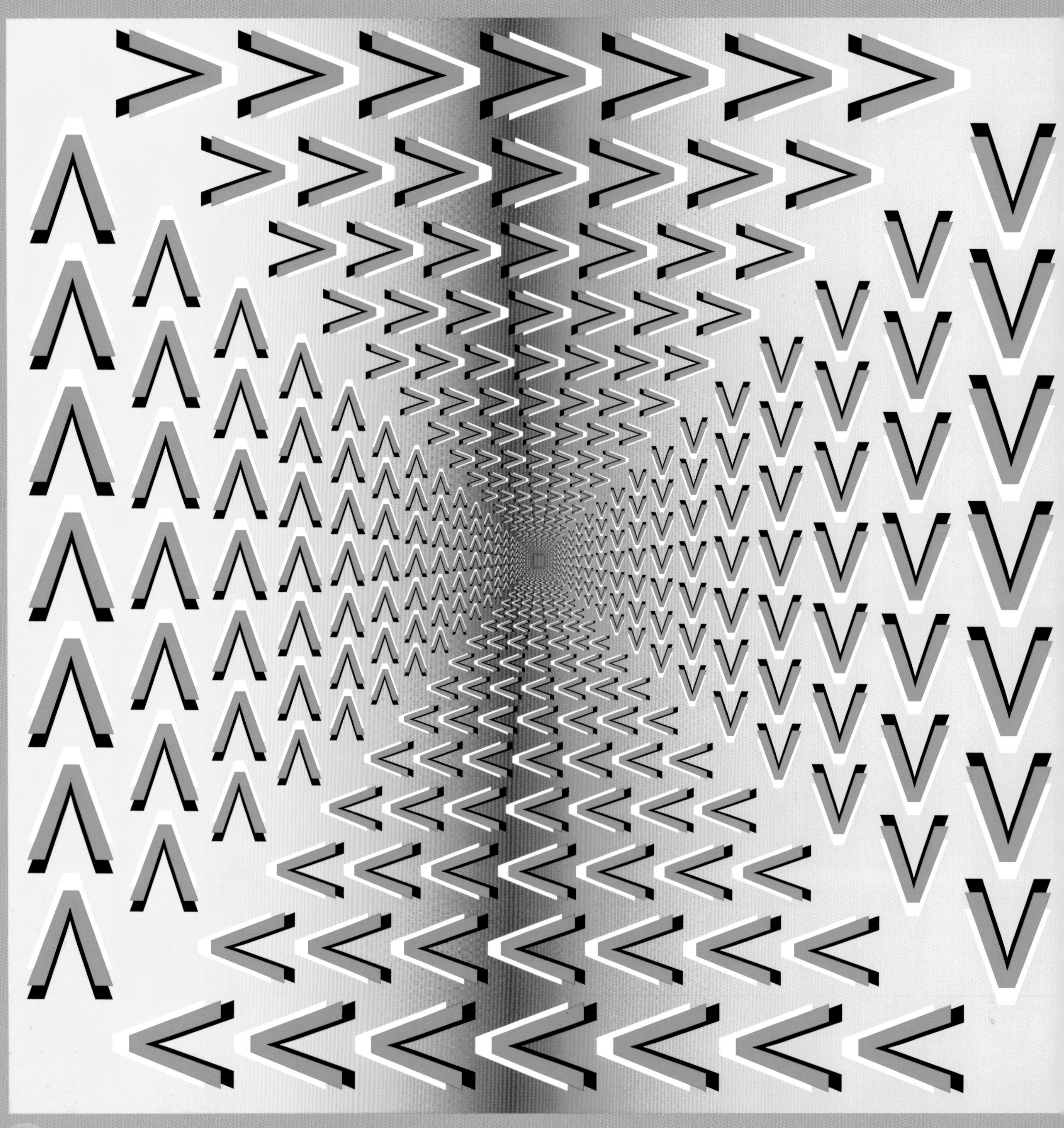

Drifting *About*

Both of these images sway from side to side as you move your eyes across them.

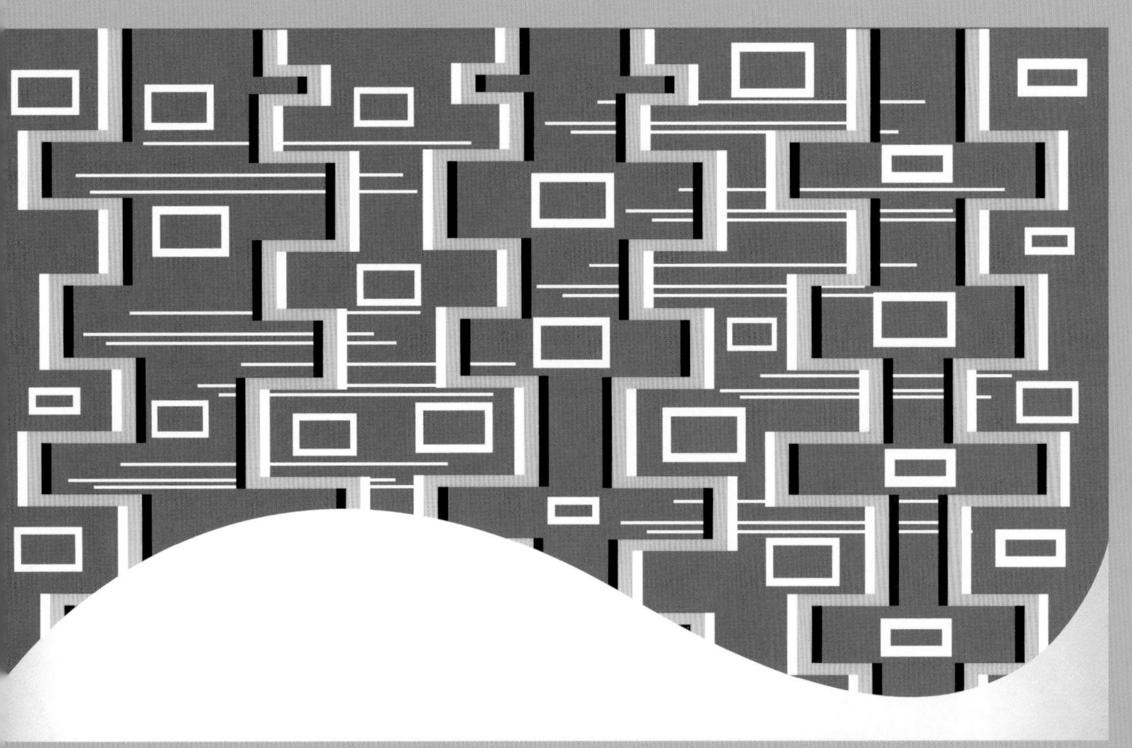

The columns in the image to the left seem to sway back and forth. If you have trouble seeing this effect, try moving your eyes directly across from this text to the centre of the image and then pausing for a moment.

Move your eyes diagonally across the image below for maximum effect.

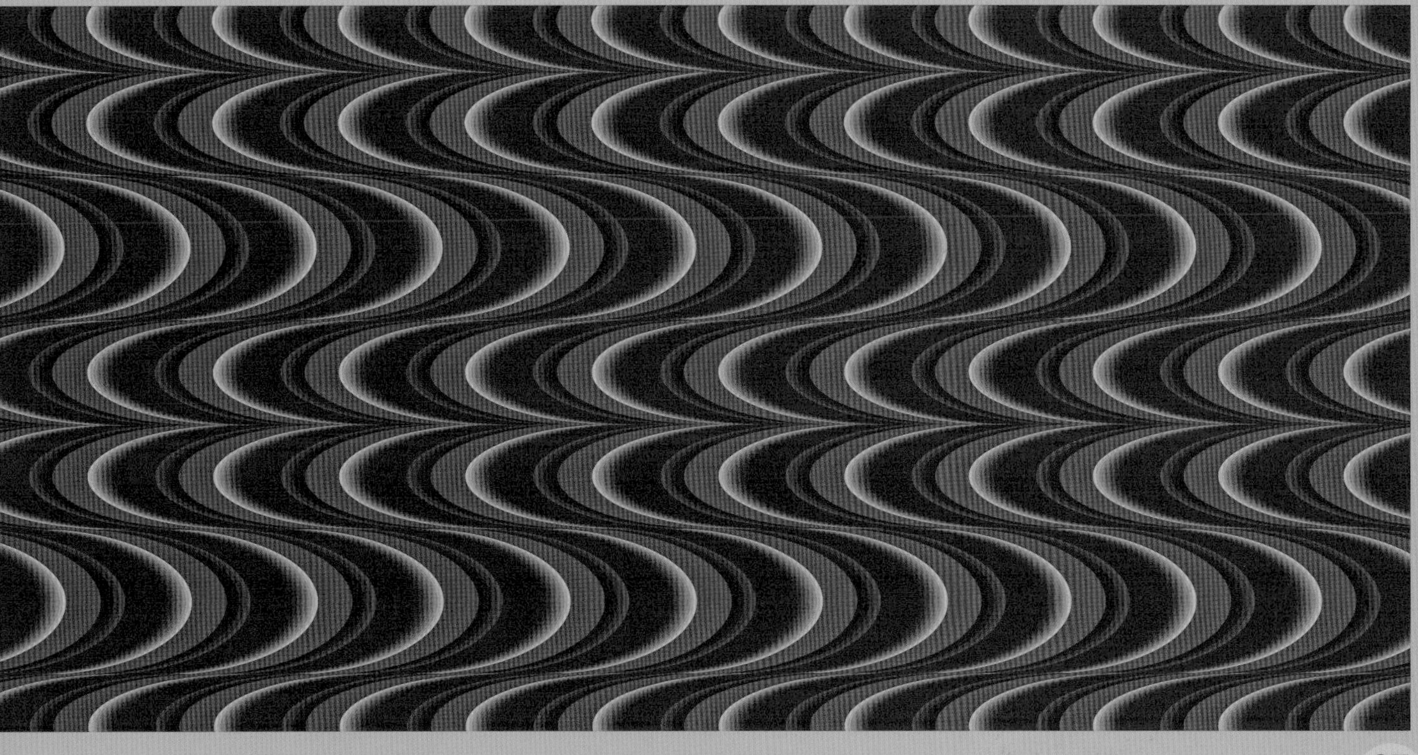

Spin the Plates

These decorative plates will rotate as you look from one plate centre to another.

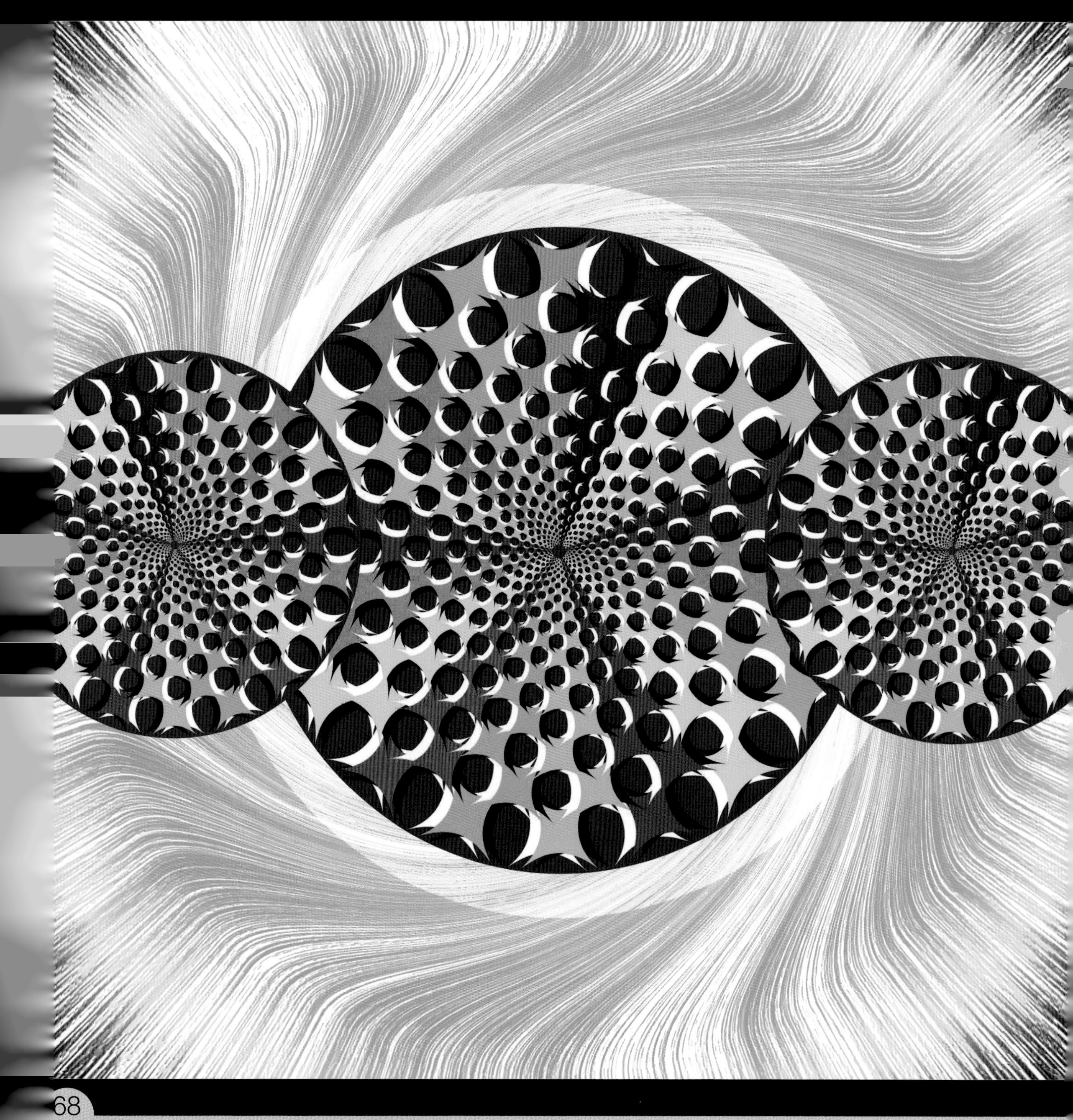

Water-lily *Display*

These beautiful lilies will unfurl in the water as you look around the display.

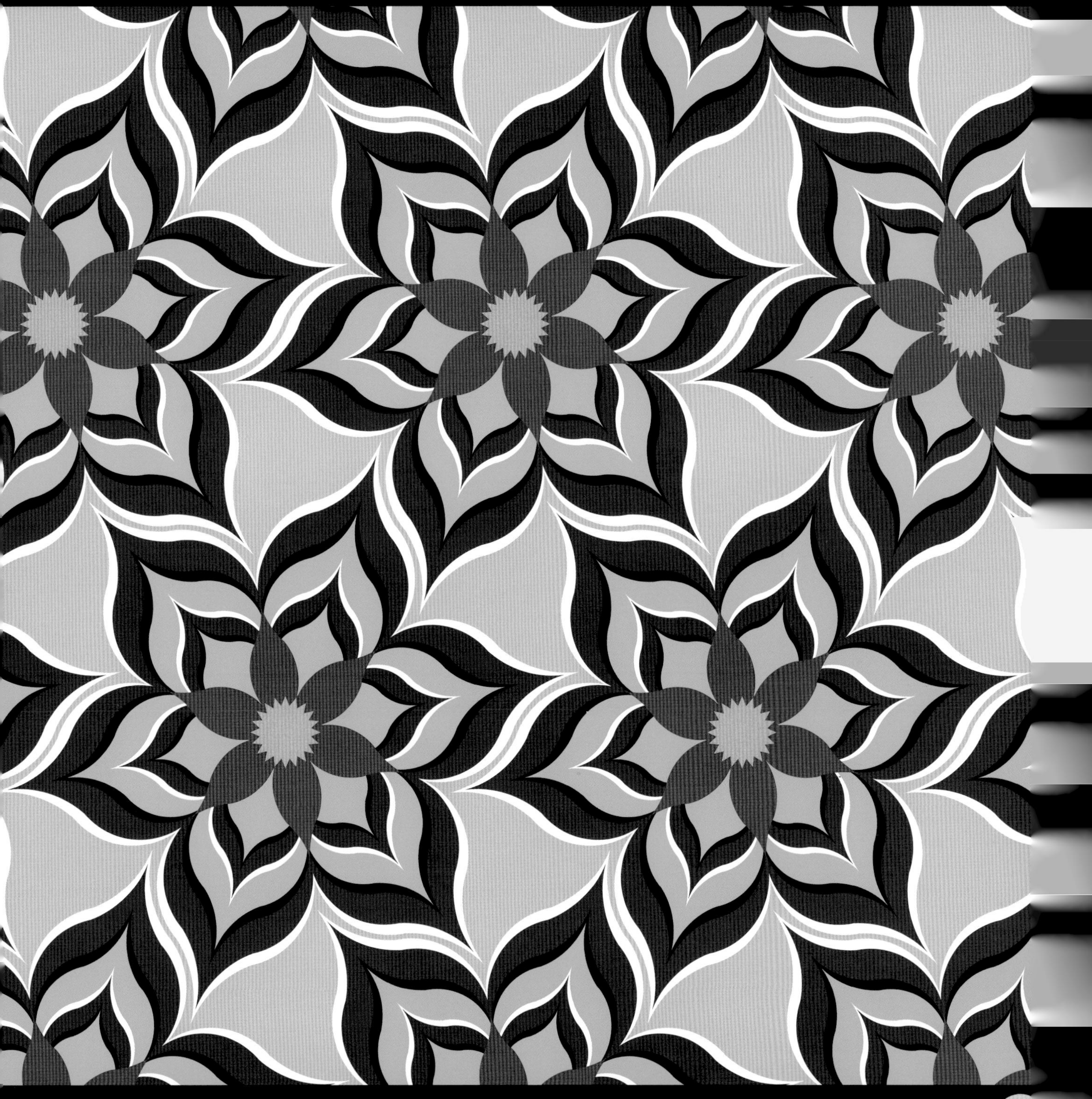

Bean **Bonanza**

Look from one edge to another and you will see these beans start to boogie.

Tunnel of Trembling

Look at the edge, then move your gaze slowly to the centre as the tunnel trembles.

Maelstrom

This storm twists and turns as you look at a corner or edge of the image.

Abstraction *Distraction*

Don't hold the book too close, then let your eyes wander around these shapes.

Spiky *Spinners*

Let your gaze wander around the edges of this image. Watch out for spikes!

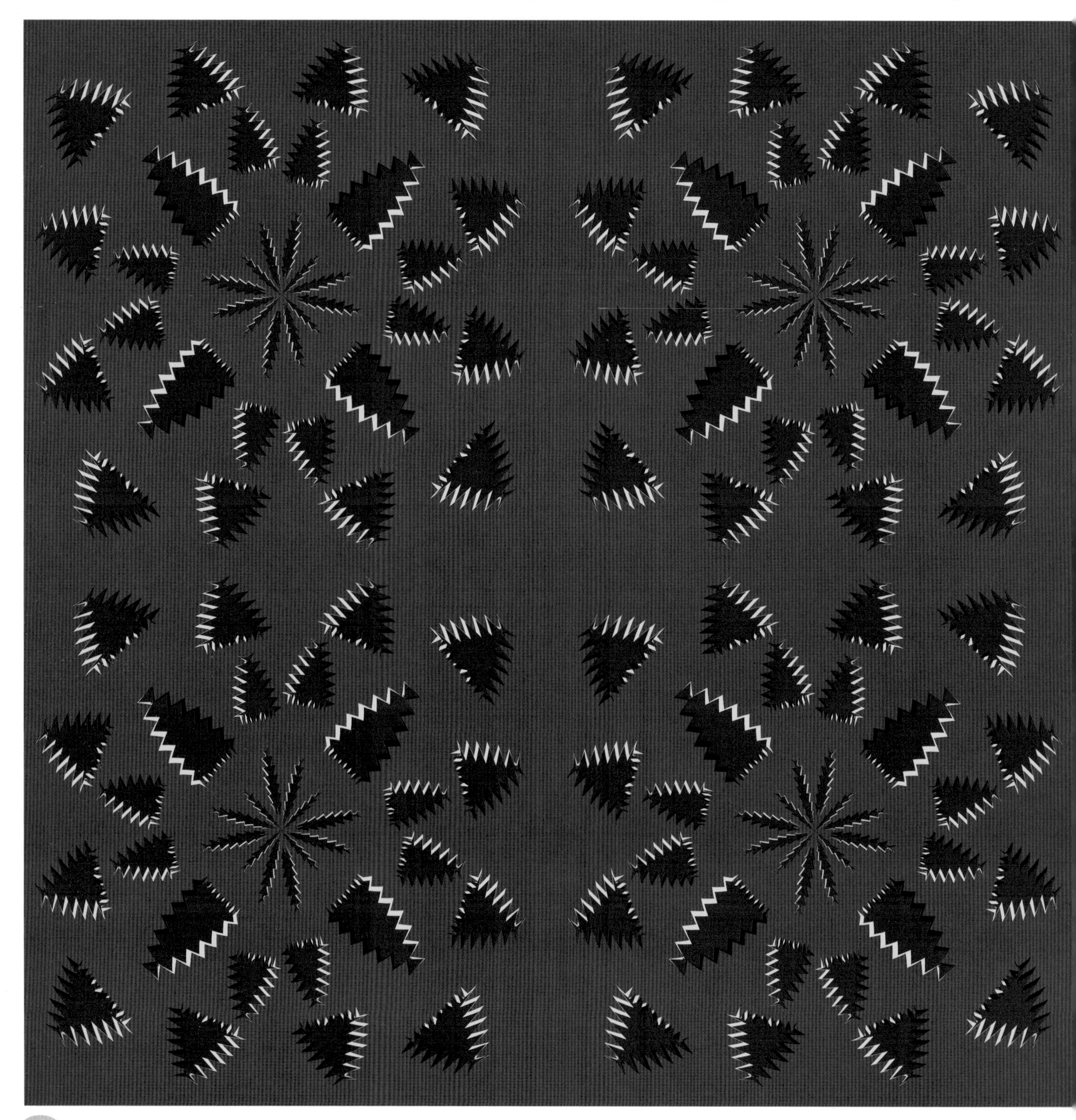

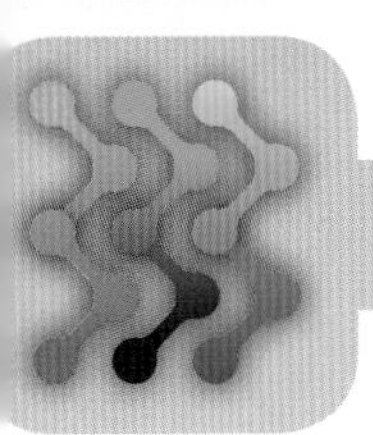

Matting and Matches

Look at the gaps in these images and you may catch them moving.

This tablemat pattern has a disturbing tendency to appear to shift around as you look at it, thanks to the particular arrangement of the overlapping yellow dots.

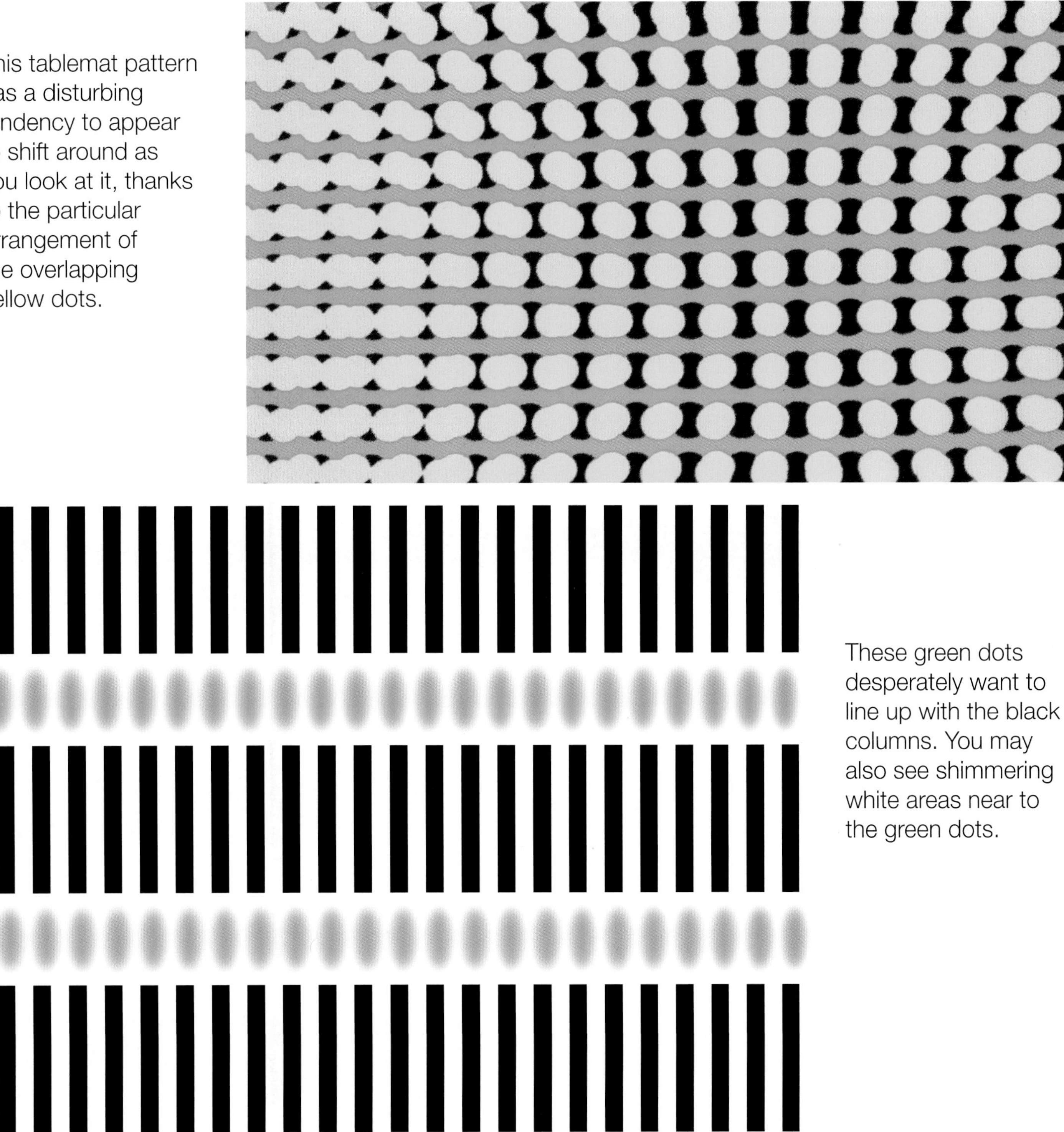

These green dots desperately want to line up with the black columns. You may also see shimmering white areas near to the green dots.

Sunny Shimmering

These strange blue shapes appear to float in front of the Sun, shifting in the haze.

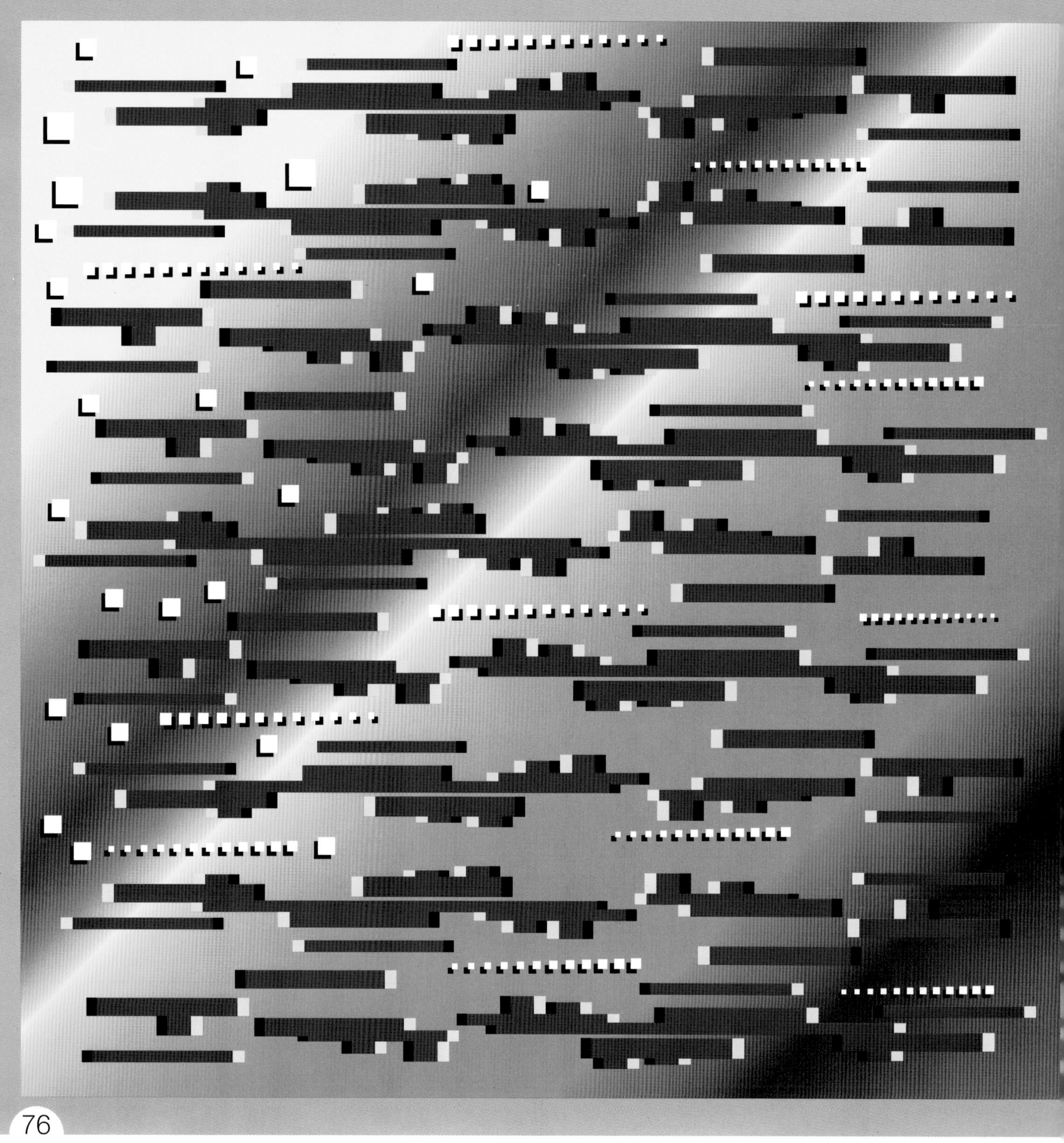

Attack of the **Dots**

Roll your eyes over these dots, as they roll on by in billowing waves.

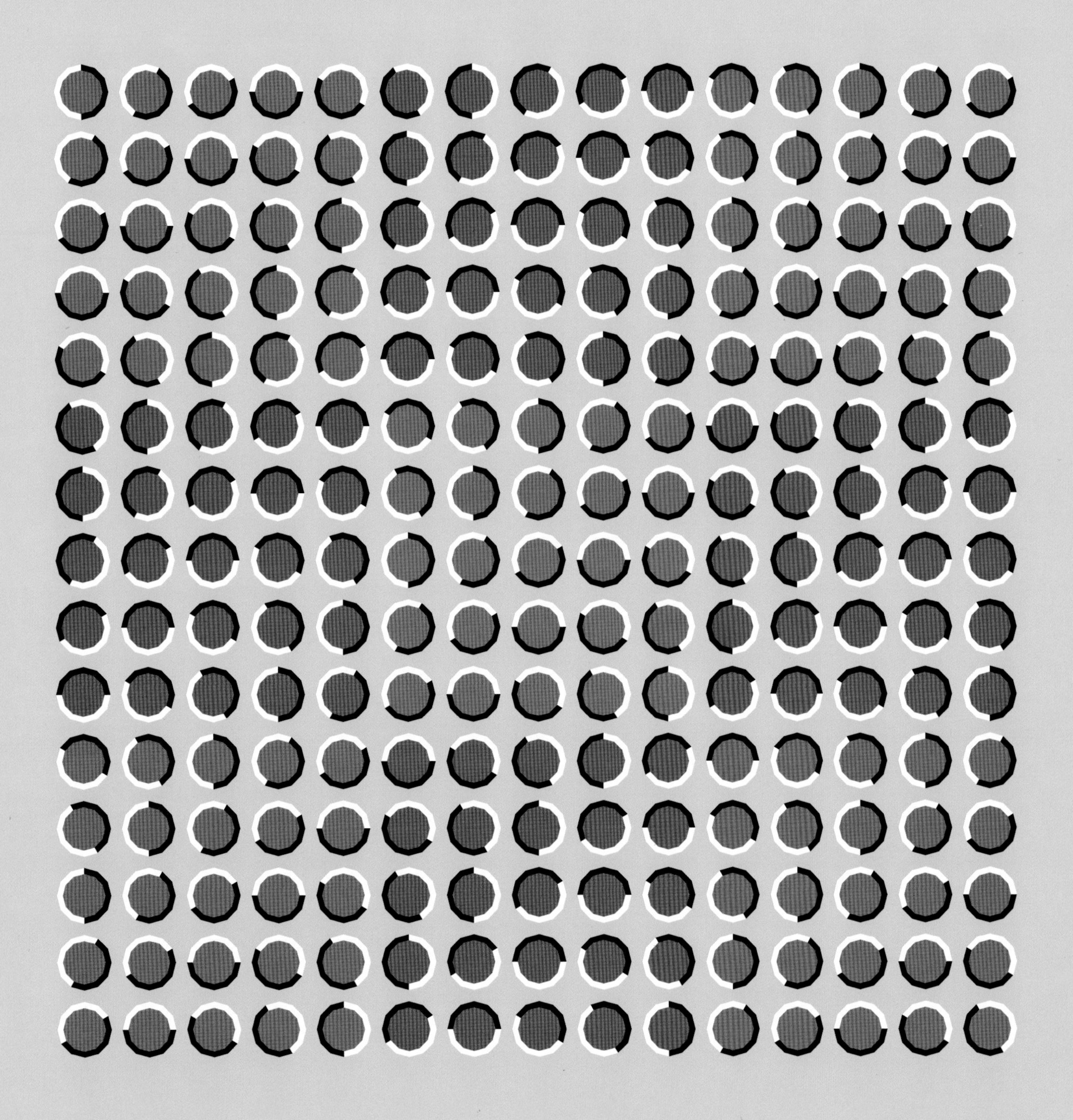

Disco Discs

These disco balls sparkle with rotating light as you move your eyes around them.

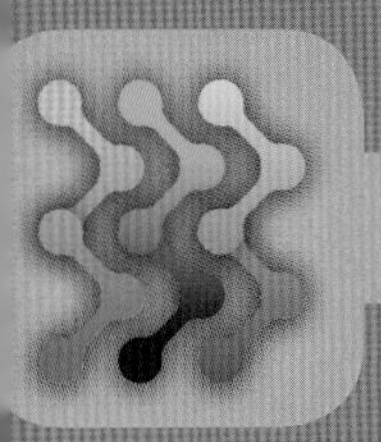

Fountain **Flow**

Look at the centres of the sprays, pausing now and again as the display plays out.

Hypnotic Light

Look slowly around this image, and it will hypnotize you with its movement.

Hypnotic Night

Look from the stars to the Moon, and the bats will start to flock.

Wave the Chequered Flag

In this case the flag will wave itself – just let your eyes wander around it freely.

Red-hot Revolution

Don't look at the Sun – but make an exception here, to see it turning.

Buzzing Bars

Look at the green and yellow bars on this page. Do they shrink or move?

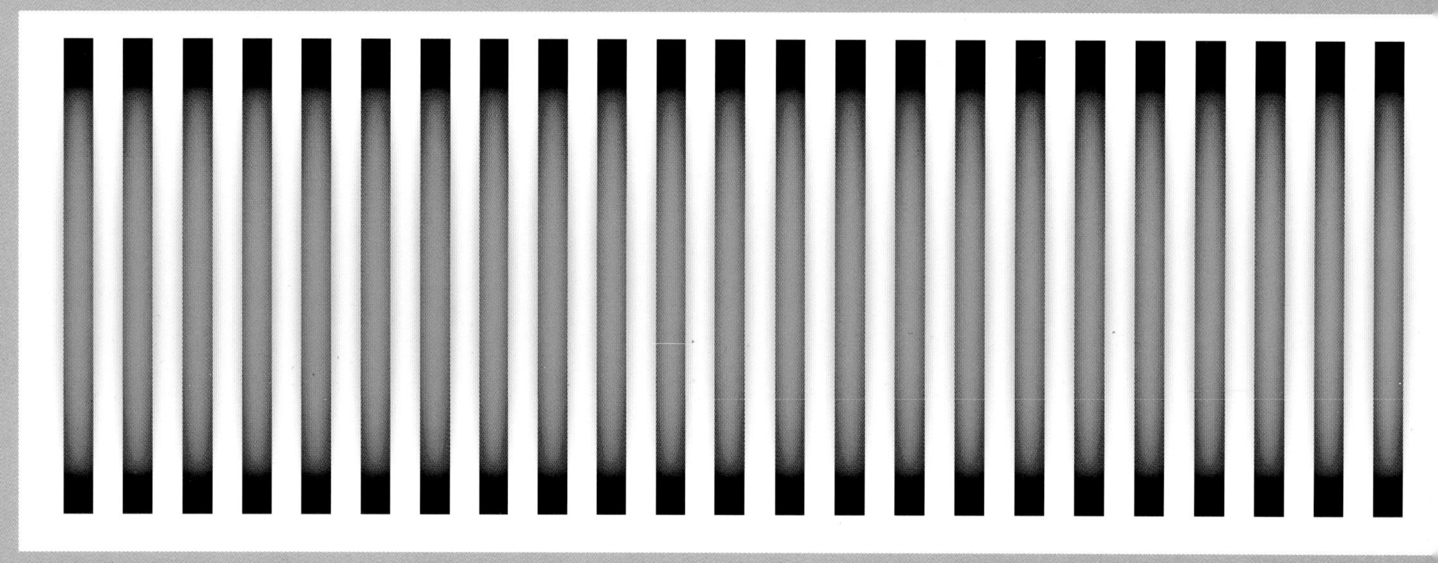

When you focus on the green bars above, they may appear to shrink away and decrease in height. Meanwhile, the bars in the image below seem to alternate in height and even colour – but they are all identical, as a ruler will confirm.

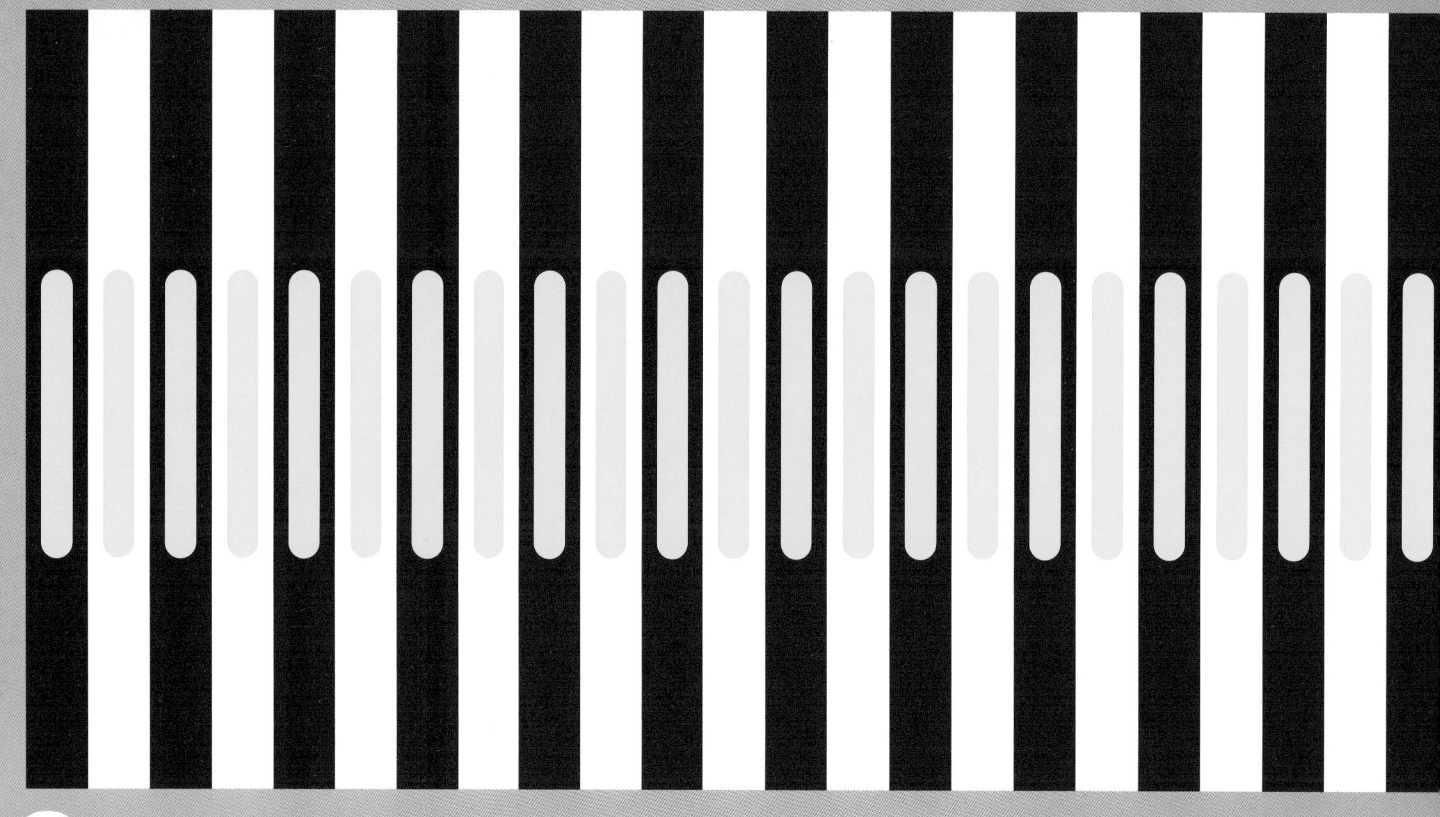

Cog-nition

Can you think how to make these cogs start to turn?

Square **Dance**

Make these grids of squares dance by moving your eyes diagonally across them.

Growing and Shrinking

Focus on the centre and move the book toward you, then away. What happens?

Room of Confusion

Move back from this image as you run your eyes diagonally down from top right.

Transporter Beams

Stare into the centre, and get ready to beam up.

It Came From **Space**

Follow the tangled mesh of this red net, as you appear to travel right through it.

Twist and **Turn**

Run your eyes in columns up and down this image, to see the pattern come alive.

Love is in the ***Air***

Move your eyes randomly around this image, and the hearts will gently flutter.

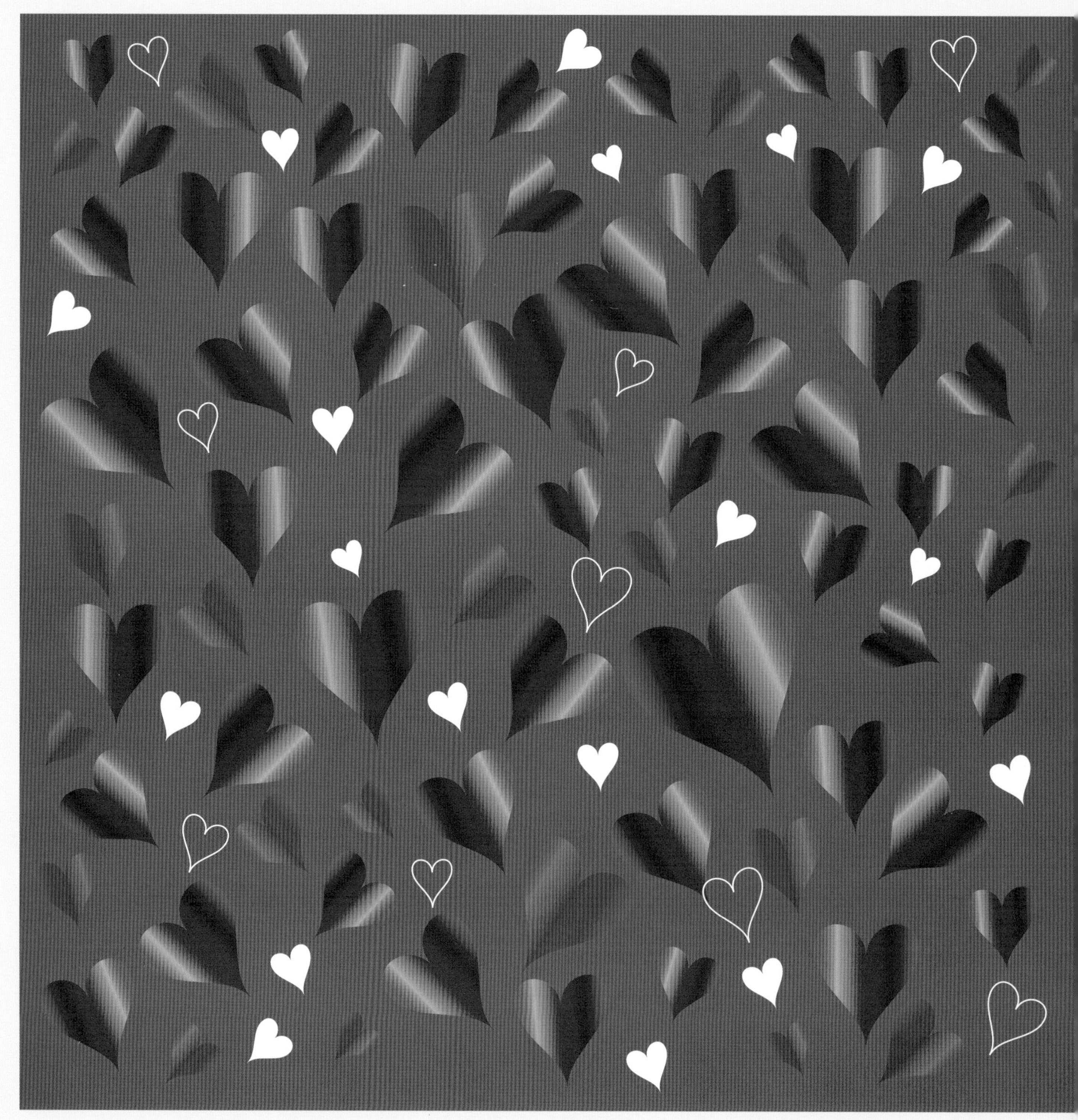

Lucky Clover

The clover will sway in a hidden breeze as you look along each row of leaves.

The **Eyes** Have It

These eyes move – but only when you're not looking at them directly!

Goodb-eye

Stare into the eye and the page will seem to suck into the space behind it.

Picture **Credits**

Find out who created each of the images in this book.

pp. 1, 6, 7, 8, 9, 10, 11, 12, 13, 18, 19 (bottom), 20, 22, 23 (bottom), 26, 28, 29, 30, 33, 34, 38, 40, 41 (top), 42, 43, 45, 47, 48, 51, 52, 53, 54, 55, 57, 58, 59 (left), 62, 63, 65, 66, 67 (top), 67 (bottom), 68, 72, 73, 74, 76, 78, 79, 80, 81, 83, 85, 88, 89, 90, 92, 93, 94, 95 Mark Grenier/Shutterstock.com
pp. 2-3 Lyudmyla Kharlamova/Shutterstock.com
p. 4 (central Sun illusion) viphotos/Shutterstock.com
pp. 4-5 (Sun rays illusion), 60, 75 (bottom), 84 (top), 84 (bottom) Gareth Moore/Any Puzzle Media Ltd
p. 14 iulias/Shutterstock.com
pp. 15, 37, 41 (bottom), 59 (right), 77 Skripnichenko Tatiana/Shutterstock.com
pp. 16, 19 (top), 27, 32, 36, 50, 56 (top), 86 (top) eurovector/Shutterstock.com
pp. 17, 71, 87 Objowl/Shutterstock.com
p. 21 (top) HunThomas/Shutterstock.com
p. 21 (bottom) COSMOKIDZ/Shutterstock.com
pp. 23 (top), 44 Betacam-SP/Shutterstock.com
pp. 24, 25, 31, 35, 46, 49, 56 (bottom), 61, 69 Andrey Korshenkov/Shutterstock.com
p. 39 Silvia Popa/Shutterstock.com
p. 64 patternlover/Shutterstock.com
p. 70 diskoVisnja/Shutterstock.com
p. 75 (top) Yuri9179126124/Shutterstock.com
pp. 82, 86 (bottom) SSylenko/Shutterstock.com
p. 91 tashechka/Shutterstock.com
p. 96 dipego/Shutterstock.com
pp. 5-95 (page header movement icons) radoma/Shutterstock.com